THE ANTHOLOGY OF BALAJI

THE ANTHOLOGY OF BALAJI

A Guide to Technology,
Truth, and Building the Future

ERIC JORGENSON

Illustrations by JACK BUTCHER

SMART FRIENDS

THE ANTHOLOGY OF BALAJI
A Guide to Technology, Truth, and Building the Future

FIRST EDITION

ISBN   978-1-5445-4292-8 *Hardcover*
       978-1-5445-4291-1 *Paperback*
       978-1-5445-4290-4 *Ebook*
       978-1-5445-4273-7 *Audiobook*

FOR MY PARTNER, MY PERSON, JEANNINE.
I LOVE YOU FOREVER. YES, REALLY.

CONTENTS

NOTES ON THIS BOOK

I built this book entirely out of transcripts, tweets, and talks Balaji has shared. Every attempt is made to present Balaji in his own words. However, a few important points remain:

→ Transcripts have been edited for clarity and brevity (multiple times).
→ I can't be 100 percent certain of every source's authenticity.
→ Please verify phrasing with a primary source before citing Balaji from this text.
→ **Please interpret generously.**

By definition, everything in this book is taken out of context. Interpretations will change over time. Understand that the original intent may be different from your interpretation in a different time, format, and context.

In the process of creating this book, I may have mistakenly re-contextualized, misinterpreted, or misunderstood things. As content passed through time, space, and medium, phrasing may have shifted in flight. Every effort has been made to maintain the original intent, but errors are (very) possible.

All brilliance in this book is Balaji's; any mistakes are mine.

TWEETS

Tweets are formatted like pull quotes but are unique content. I use them to summarize or punctuate an idea from the main text.

> This formatting shows I'm quoting a tweet from Balaji.

SKIP AROUND

This is a choose-your-own adventure book. Jump to anything that interests you and skip anything that doesn't. Though be aware, ideas often build on previous ideas.

LOOK IT UP

Balaji uses some uncommon technical words. If you find a word or concept you're not familiar with, look it up and learn something. It's what Balaji would want.

CITATIONS

We've removed individual citations from the published version for smoother reading. All sources are available in the Bonus Section, and a fully cited version is available on BalajiAnthology.com.

INTRODUCTION

BY BALAJI SRINIVASAN

I was a little reticent about the very idea of a biography of a living person, namely myself!

But in today's world, you have four choices when it comes to coverage of yourself.

1. Pseudonymous. First, you can remain pseudonymous*, like Satoshi. I recommend this.
2. Direct. Second, you can go direct and publish your own content. I recommend this too.
3. Reactive. Third, you can cooperate with hostile corporate journalists, like when Peter Thiel's associates made the mistake of talking to a professional hater like Max Chafkin for his book-length attack.
4. Positive. Finally, you can block all corporate journalists and instead just help positive people who get what you're doing, like when Peter Thiel's associates spoke with an intelligent writer like Jimmy Soni for his book-length exegesis.

When enumerated this way, it seems obvious that you want some combination of 1, 2, and 4.

But conflict is attention, and it's very easy to just default into responding to negativity. This is partly because negativity is louder than positivity on the internet. Those who like what you're doing will just hit the like button, but those who dislike it will send angry missives. To not get trapped in being reactive, you have to intentionally focus on the positive. And Eric Jorgenson is very positive, so I said, "All right, write the book, and I'll write the Introduction."

But this then led to my second quandary.

See, to write an Introduction, you need to know who a book is for. I wasn't sure whether this book would exactly fit into what we might call the tech-self-help section, the (useful) kind of business books and self-improvement books that fans of Tim Ferriss and Andrew Huberman read.

Because while I've had reasonable success as a founder and investor, there are certainly people who are better company founders (like my friend Brian Armstrong, founder of Coinbase) and people who are much more focused on being great investors (like my friend Naval Ravikant, founder of AngelList). I can give advice on how to build and invest in billion dollar companies, and you'll find some of that in this book...but there are people who are even better.

Similarly, I'm a good engineer (but Vitalik Buterin is better), a respectable scientist (but Vijay Pande is better), a decent turn-around CEO (but Ben Horowitz is better), a bestselling author (but Tim Ferriss is better), and so on. I sit at the intersection of many existing categories—founder, investor, engineer, scientist, CEO, tech executive, content creator, author, etc.—without really considering myself defined by any of them.

I suppose what I really am is the id of technology.

The one who says what tech thinks.

And what do I say?

→ That the internet is to the USA what the Americas once were to the UK—a frontier territory, where all the action is.
→ That just as the Western frontier once gave rise to an American pioneer class, the internet frontier has given rise to a global technology class.
→ That this class is not defined by inherited wealth (many are born poor in places like India and China), nor by legacy institutions (many are born anti-institutionalists), but by the ability to create wealth and the desire to found new institutions.
→ And that these new institutions will eventually include not just new companies and new currencies, but new cities—and even new countries.

This is the concept elaborated on in my book, *The Network State*. It's also now the view of many in tech who realize that just as it was easier to start Bitcoin than to reform the Fed, it will actually be easier to start a new city than to reform San Francisco, and easier to start a new country than to reform the FDA.

Perhaps it will be your view too.

See my talk on the pseudonymous economy. This is already emerging: it's an internet where you separate your speaking name from your official name as a matter of course, such that any attacks are attacks on your arguments rather than your character.

ERIC'S INTRODUCTION

Have you ever wanted to sit with Balaji Srinivasan and spend a few hours deep in conversation? That's exactly what this book feels like. Here, you can absorb all his biggest ideas to apply them to your own life.

I created this book from hundreds of hours of podcasts, posts, and tweets he has produced in the past decade. By collecting, selecting, curating, and threading them together in this book, I've given you the best of Balaji in a few hours of reading.

Balaji is a brilliant entrepreneur, engineer, investor, and futurist. His ideas are unique, insightful, and often divisive. You may not like or agree with what you read here—but you will think new thoughts and see the world differently by the end.

My favorite books give me a new type of X-ray vision. They teach me how to see new layers of the world I didn't understand or even notice before. I gained a new lens on the world from this book. I hope you find the same joy.

I find myself living differently after writing this book. It inspired investments (drone construction, nuclear reactors, robotic limbs) and health changes (so I might live to 120+). The ideas in this book give me an appreciation for our place in the history unfolding today and impatience for the many ways we're punching ourselves in the face.

This book has three parts. First, it describes what technology has done for us and what it can do in the future. Second, it presents the types of truth and how to evaluate ideas for yourself. The third part is packed with Balaji's tactical advice for starting a company (or protocol, nonprofit, project, or country). Finally, so you can learn to think like Balaji, his recommended reading list is in the Bonus section. You can derive his worldview by reading his most influential books.

Technology has driven our past and will shape our future. Emerging technologies show mind-blowing promise. After reading this, you will start seeing new opportunities everywhere.

Truth plays a key role in this book. There is a constant clamor of information today. It can be crazy-making to figure out who is honest and what is true. This is a huge challenge, an important problem to solve. We need the tools to think for ourselves despite biased, corrupt, or adversarial information. (Expect this part to shake you up a bit!)

Technology (Part I) and Truth (Part II) are your sword and shield in the quest to build something useful. Building the Future (Part III) is a map to the grail. These ideas will equip you to change your life, your community, and maybe the future of our species.

(The first part is the most important, but the last part is my favorite.)

Though it is full of Balaji's ideas, this book is actually a guide to thinking for yourself. Discover your own way to build the future you want to see. You might find your next great investment, start a billion-dollar company, or found an entirely new country.

Does Balaji sometimes sound a bit like a comic book villain? Maybe. He is an eccentric genius, after all. Have a conversation with this book. Adopt the ideas that serve you and wrestle with the others. When you're done reading, put the book down and get to work.

Our future is born anew every day. Use your powers well.

Create a product. Solve a problem. Build.

Onward,
Eric Jorgenson
Kansas City

PS: Wondering if I want to invest in what you decide to build? The answer is probably, "Hell yes!" So please reach out. There are dozens of enormous, world-changing opportunities Balaji shows us in this book. Let's build them together.

If you enjoy the ideas in this book, you will love my podcast, *Smart Friends.* Go to EJorgenson.com and enter your email to get new episodes and notes on what I learn.

TIMELINE OF BALAJI SRINIVASAN

→ 1980–1997: Born and raised in Plainview, New York.

→ 1998–2006 (AGE 18–26): Earned a BS, MS, and PhD in electrical engineering and MS in chemical engineering from Stanford for work in genetic circuits and computational genomics.

→ 2006–2007 (AGE 26–27): Taught statistics and bioinformatics at Stanford.

→ 2008 (AGE 28): Co-founded Counsyl, a clinical genomics company.

→ 2013 (AGE 33): Began angel investing, including investing in Bitcoin at ~$10.

→ 2013 (AGE 33): Taught Stanford's Startup Engineering online course with 250,000+ students, one of the first online courses about Bitcoin.

→ 2013 (AGE 33): Co-founded the company which eventually became Earn.com.

→ 2013 (AGE 33): Joined venture capital firm Andreessen Horowitz as a General Partner.

→ 2014 (AGE 34): Co-founded Coin Center, now the leading nonprofit in crypto.

→ 2015–2023 (AGE 35–43+): Seed investor in hundreds of tech

startups and digital assets, including Ethereum, Solana, Avalanche, Replit, Bloom, Superhuman, Opensea, and many more.

→ 2018 (AGE 38): Earn.com was acquired by Coinbase.

→ 2018 (AGE 38): Counsyl, the clinical genomics company, was sold for $375M.

→ 2018 (AGE 38): Balaji became CTO of Coinbase. (There he led the rewrite of the Coinbase backend to support hundreds of new assets, launched USDC, closed $1B for Coinbase Custody, integrated Coinbase Earn, closed $200M+ in Coinbase Earn airdrops, and built the crypto engineering team.)

→ 2019 (AGE 39): Balaji completed his stint at Coinbase.

→ 2020 (AGE 40): Forecasted the consequences of COVID-19 months early on Twitter.

→ 2022 (AGE 42): Published *The Network State*, which became a WSJ bestseller.

→ 2023 (AGE 43+): To be *determined...*

Now, here is Balaji in his own words...

BACKGROUND

I grew up on Long Island in New York. Both of my parents were physicians. They were immigrants from India, in a time and culture where long-distance calls were expensive and mail was slow. They were cut off from their home culture. Their cultural conventions worked for 1950s India—completely different from 1980s New York.

My parents were working all the time, you know. We had sick relatives, so a lot of time and money went to them. My parents were focused on their challenges. I escaped into an inner world of fiction and reading, flying through books. That was my life for many, many years.

I was born with certain advantages. My grandfather taught me a lot of math early on, before he passed away. I learned to read at a young age. But the good comes with the bad.

The first thirteen years of my conscious life, school was a prison-like environment. You must go there every day; you cannot leave. You have no control over your environment. You cannot avoid other kids in school, and I was simply not part of the social network. This was pre-internet, so I had no cultural role models. Especially early on, I was dressed up in foreign clothes while all of the other kids were wearing sports t-shirts. I stuck out.

Being the only brown kid among hundreds of people, lots of kids would gang up on you and call you "Gandhi," and you could say, "That's not an insult," and run, but they'd just chase you. I learned that the first guy who comes at me, I need to hit him—bam!—with a book and just act crazy so the other guys don't jump on me. Later, at the principal's office, the assailants would have "crocodile tears" about how the little Indian boy had started the fight. Their parents knew the principal, and he'd say, "Balaji, why did you attack young Jimmy and Jamie?" I learned early on that you've got to stand up for yourself, that the fix is in...the state is against you.

In short, the teachers wouldn't protect me, so I learned to fight. I learned how to deter aggression and how to find a defensible position. I had to develop the reputation of being crazy. I learned the establishment was not on my side.

I ended up in detention a lot. Detention was great, because I could read in peace. At the front of the school were rankings of students on the honor roll and in detention. I was always at the top of both.

Eventually I got enough context on American culture to learn how to fit in. I started lifting weights and made the varsity football and lacrosse teams in high school. There was a policy of no cuts if you were persistent, so I made it through "hell week" in the summer and became the n-th string cornerback and midfielder. I'd never be the world's greatest athlete, but I was in great physical condition by the end of high school and still have the build from years of squats and power cleans.

This was a useful experience for me because I learned to strengthen things that were previously weak areas. I brought an area up from a zero to a five out of ten just by grinding through it. It was also helpful for me to learn my limitations, to learn humility—unlike an academic topic, no matter how much I practiced lacrosse, I'd never be as good as someone who just had the instincts for it. Knowing what I was weak at allowed me to become strong.

Those are my character traits. "Good at math," "disobedient," "grind when I have to," and "harshly assess my weaknesses." This was a disadvantage early on, but it paid off later in life.

The benefits of disobedience (or "intellectual assertiveness") kept increasing. It started extremely negatively, being kicked out of classes in high school. In academia it started to become a positive, because I had observations others didn't, and it helped me pursue more unique work.

In venture capital and content creation, originality is really, really valued. Whether you call it originality, being disobedient, or being contrarian—the combination of being analytical and not fully obedient has been important.

> I come from the generation before the internet was really useful.

I graduated high school in 1997. The search engines weren't that good, and Wikipedia didn't exist. I feel like my education really commenced in 2001 when Google got good enough for me to start leveling up on the internet, self-educating, drinking it all in.

If you've seen a movie where someone is frozen in a block of ice before they thaw and get to experience the world—that's what life felt like to me before going to college. Everything moved in very slow motion until college. Then things sped up a lot.

At Stanford, I got a BS, MS, and PhD in electrical engineering and an MS in chemical engineering. It was an exciting time in genomics, because the Human Genome Project was going on. I chose a major to expose me to genomics while also having the maximum amount of math. Chemical engineering was the answer.

The specific work I did in grad school was genetic circuits in microbes, how viruses and microbes are wired. We studied their system diagrams and protein interaction networks, doing statistical and computational analysis of their genome sequences. That kind of work in genetic circuits or systems biology is at the intersection of electrical engineering, computer science, genomics, statistics, and biochemistry.

I founded a startup because we could get larger data samples and make a bigger difference to the world as a profitable company than in academia relying on grants. Programming and building businesses were ways to apply these new technologies more efficiently.

We started a genomics company called Counsyl, where I was the CTO and co-founder, which ended up being sold for

$375 million. We had to bootstrap for the first few years and eventually got funding from Peter Thiel and Founders Fund. We scaled to do more than one million diagnostic tests and changed the standard of care for Mendelian genetic diseases.

I am also an angel investor. In crypto, I was early to Bitcoin, Ethereum, Zcash, and others. In 2013, I became a General Partner at Andreessen Horowitz (a16z), focusing on crypto, biomedicine, and online education. I recruited Vijay Pande to the firm and did some of the earliest bio investments in what became the a16z bio fund, including very successful companies like Benchling. I also worked with Chris Dixon, and we did several crypto investments. Some of the logistical problems with investing in Bitcoin at that time eventually motivated the a16z crypto fund. I co-founded Coin Center while at a16z and recruited Jerry Brito; this became the leading nonprofit in the crypto space. I also helped take the firm into regulated industries, at the interface between software, the physical world, and the political environment.

In 2015, I took over one of our portfolio companies at a16z, to turn it around. That became Earn.com, which was acquired by Coinbase, so I became the CTO of Coinbase for a while. There, I integrated Earn.com to create Coinbase Earn with a team of folks. This became a multi-hundred-million dollar business for Coinbase.

Stanford invited me to teach computer science and statistics for several years. I also taught an open online course about startup engineering with 250,000 students worldwide. The course fused technology and philosophy. It talked about why to do a startup and difficulties that arise—what I wish I had known as a PhD student starting my first company.

> I like to think of myself as a pragmatic ideologue.

I have a long-term horizon; I have my eyes set on the long-term goal of transhumanism. But I'm willing to be pragmatic and execute in the short run. I go down the to-do list toward that North Star. I'm always conscious of the long term.

Every few years, I feel like my life starts anew. I'm in my forties now, but I feel like I've just started because I built up various resources like distribution, network, and capital. Now I can broadcast ideas, invest money, and see big things happen.

The past has all been the prologue. Now I've got a canvas to play with. Some people make a bit of money and go sit on the beach. I think of money as a stick of dynamite. It is leverage to go and blow up the obstacles in the path of my next goal.

I'd like to see us ethically and technologically aligned on progress. I'd like to see humanity believing math is good. Believing generating nuclear power is good. Believing getting to Mars is good. Believing expanding is good.

Let's get on the long-term track toward ascent. In my lifetime, I want to see humanity working together to grow toward infinity.

> Immutable money, infinite frontier, eternal life.

PART I

TECHNOLOGY

Putting in a lot of labor doesn't necessarily generate value.

Putting in the right technology often does.

THE VALUE OF TECHNOLOGY

BUILDING WHAT MONEY CAN'T BUY

I'm not money motivated. I know some people are. I wear the same T-shirts I wore in grad school. I don't own cars or anything like that. I look at money as a tool to build things I can't buy today.

Elon Musk is building SpaceX because he can't buy a trip to Mars. You can have all the money in the world, but you can't buy a trip to Mars. One hundred years ago, the richest man in the world couldn't buy an iPhone. That's the kind of progress I care about.

We don't have an unambiguous metric for progress. If you must pick one, we can make a strong case for life expectancy. In that area, progress was exponential but has recently decelerated—and even reversed.

Life expectancy used to be *the* metric of technological progress. More recently, people are focused on stock prices or GDP, which are fine, but they are ultimately subjective human metrics as opposed to objective physical metrics like age.

We have to start talking more about our values than our valuations. Money is only a tool. What really matters is building something you can't buy. That's how we actually improve metrics like life expectancy.

True technologists should aspire to change physical metrics. We can change life expectancy from 70 years old to 150. We need to focus on truly transformative technologies—not just life extension, but brain-machine interfaces, limb regeneration, curing deafness with RNA injections, and curing blindness with bionic eyes. We can make actual miracles with technology today.

The emotional case for technology:

→ Why accept 30k deaths/year rather than speed up the development of self-driving cars?
→ Why let regulators prevent us from creating life-saving biomedicine?
→ Why accept non-accidental death at all, rather than pushing life extension?

Using technology to be high-agency is definitely something I believe in. Of course you should use the best possible tool. Why wouldn't you? If you're trying to move something and a lever is right there on the ground, why would you not use that?

Often people don't want to use a new tool or technology. They want to do things the way they always have because learning how to use that lever is new. They are uncertain and afraid. What happens if the lever breaks? What are the risks in using the lever? Why don't we just lift it with our bodies like we've always done?

I think it is ridiculously, obviously good to use the better technologies. That is still much more rare than you might think.

> Science is theory. Technology is practice. It's
> applied science.

Referring to "the tech industry" is dumb. That's a label we kind of accept, but it's not a clear thought. You would not call something "the physics industry." Every industry uses technology, like every industry uses physics.

Business is simply a vehicle to push the future forward and drive human progress. Whether that is accomplished through an open source project, an academic paper, or a research lab, the tool doesn't matter. The goal is to advance technology. Build a better steam engine. It may turn out the best way of doing that is with a capitalist vehicle, but nowadays it could be done with an on-chain community or a crowdfund. The tool is less important than the goal.

If the purpose of technology is to reduce scarcity, then the ultimate purpose of technology is to eliminate mortality.

At first that sounds crazy. But let's start here: the purpose of technology is to reduce scarcity. Think about how a breakthrough is described: faster, smaller, cheaper, better. All these words mean that with a new technology, we can do more with less.

Mortality is the main source of scarcity. If we had more time (or infinite time), we would be less concerned with whether something was faster. The reason speed has value is because time has value; the reason time has value is because human life spans are finite.

If you make life spans longer, you reduce the effective cost of everything. If reducing scarcity is the purpose of technology, eliminating the main source of scarcity—mortality—is the ultimate purpose of technology. Life extension is the most important thing we can invent.

We need to evangelize technological progress with every word and action. To recognize that the purpose of technology is to transcend our limits and to motivate everything we do with this sense of purpose. To take the winnings from our web apps and put them toward Mars. To feel no hesitation to start small and no shame in dreaming big. To tell the world it is possible to cure the deaf, restore sight, and end death itself.

VALUE CREATION COMES FROM TECHNOLOGY

Some people believe value comes directly from labor. They price something based on the number of labor hours that went into it. If it takes five hours of a surgeon's time to do some procedure, it will be really expensive. If it takes one hour, then it is cheaper.

At first that seems reasonable, except *people pay for the value provided to them.* They pay for the impact on them, not the cost to provide it.

It might take a lot of time for you to handcraft one chair, but a chair manufactured on an assembly line may be cheaper and better. Even though the first chair might have more labor going into it, the second chair may cost less and have higher quality.

Rather than the "labor theory of value," I think about the "technology theory of value." The actual value injection is from technology. Think about using a light bulb rather than having humans running around with you holding candles. It's the same for refrigerators and automobiles.

> Technology theory of value is better than labor theory of value.

This is the technology theory of value: technology is actually where the value creation is happening. We can see this most clearly on the computer.

Accelerating robotics means more and more value is created on the computer. We don't fully realize this because today we see software affecting only screens. Once more robot arms are moving the physical world, that will change.

Eventually, everything we can think of basically will be reduced to software. All the non-software components are gradually going to get commoditized. We're going to robotify a lot of things. We will have self-driving trucks and fully robotic ports. We will talk later about generalizing the concept of printing on paper to "printing out" any material thing, like a bowl of food.

The leverage on software is only going to increase. This is where all the value creation is going to come from. It will be mainly software creating value and everything else executing it.

Technology's first law: whatever can be done over the internet will be done over the internet. (Though it might take a while for any given phenomenon to move online.) The statement might sound obvious, but the implications are far-reaching.

> Let's unlock the value being held back by antiquated laws.

Regulation is the primary barrier for many businesses. Historically, Silicon Valley has been engaged with purely technological issues like building a faster hard drive or optimizing bandwidth. Businesses like this are built continually.

But companies using genomics or drones encounter the physical world. In that case, the main barrier is not technology. The primary risk is actually regulatory risk. Evangelizing this point was my primary focus for two years as a Venture Capitalist.

In 2009, it would have been remarkable to claim "$100 billion in equity value is being held back by outdated taxi and hotel regulations." Uber and Airbnb showed it was true. The "next big thing" was being held back by those eighty-year-old regulations. Very, very few people were thinking about them. These things are so remarkable and hard to understand that they go unseen constantly.

A philosopher named Frederic Bastiat has a parable about this, about what is seen and what is unseen. It requires more empathy and more imagination to think about value that isn't seen. You can see a skyscraper. You can't see what could have been built but wasn't. You can't see the cities we could build if we had regulations allowing skyscrapers to be built in two weeks rather than two years.

That's not a theoretical example. In China, they're building skyscrapers in two weeks flat. You can see it on YouTube. They put up a camera and build twenty-four hours a day from prefab material assembled on site. They're building 100x faster than you can build in the US. In the US, it took ten years to rebuild the World Trade Center.

Now there are diverse regulatory regimes around the world. You can see the unseen. Overseas, you see what we could have without obstinate rules. It's important to think about the unseen innovation you would have without regulation.

In 2009, outdated regulations on taxis and hotels held back $100+ billion companies. Remember $100B only shows the value captured by Uber and Airbnb. The total value created is much higher, unseen, and incalculable. How much time has been saved in parking? How much are employees paid? How much are millions of drivers and hosts paid? Yes, the companies are valuable, but the unseen benefits to all of society are on the order of a trillion dollars in value created.

Now things get really interesting. If that was just taxi and hotel regulations, what is the FDA holding back? What's the FAA holding back? What's the SEC holding back?

Regulators are well-intentioned, but most laws were written one hundred years ago. The FDA's ancestor was started in 1906. The SEC got most of its powers after the Great Depression. These laws are from two or three generations ago. In terms of technology, that is many generations.

It's quite possible we can achieve many of the objectives of these regulatory agencies with new technology in a better way.

And, as an example, I'll go back to Uber and Airbnb. If you look at their review systems, you see real-time star ratings of both the buyers and the sellers updated on a per-ride or per-stay basis. That is *much* more responsive as a regulatory system. Compare that to taxi medallions or hotel inspectors.

Regulators don't have the same level of fast, precise, digital feedback between buyer and seller. Today, if you're a bad actor, you're banned from Uber or Airbnb within a few hours. These companies are accomplishing the goals of a regulated marketplace by banning bad actors and giving low ratings to poor quality actors, without coercion. We don't have to send the police to raid and shut down a bad hotel or throw somebody in jail for an expired taxi license. We achieve the same objectives in a better way.

> Different mental models:
>
> Pass a law—force someone else to do something.
>
> Write some code—I will do something.

You can't invent planes without test pilots. We have to have early adopters.

We allow people to go bungee jumping and skydiving. We allow people to sign up for the military to fight and die overseas. There should also be room for people to take risks to advance technology.

The *CRC Handbook of Chemistry and Physics* was our textbook before the online encyclopedia of chemistry. If you look at the *CRC Handbook*, you'll see that some of the really old compounds have smell and taste listed. In the past, some chemist smelled cyanide. The last thing he did was scrawl down "smells like almonds" as he died. He took a hit for the team to advance science. (This is somewhat tongue in cheek, but there was a time when chemists would actually smell and taste things.)

Today, we don't have the same level of risk tolerance. People want an extremely high level of safety, but they don't realize we can be *too conservative*. Being too conservative on safety actually leads to systemic risk. Systemic risk happens when you stop taking risks and get stuck with a system that no longer improves.

A direct example is new medicine. Someone has to be first to try a new surgery or drug. The people taking the risk are heroes. They should get awards and prizes. As a society, we should allow this and reward them. Without someone taking that risk, millions of people won't get a cure.

Without a pilot taking risks, we don't test a new faster plane. Without the new faster plane, we lose millions of man-years of time (our lives) due to slower air travel.

This and thousands of other examples are "what is unseen."

We need jurisdictions and regulations to allow and encourage early adopters. We need early adopters even, and especially, when there is some degree of physical risk. This person may suffer injury or even die a heroic death. The pilots who sacrificed to build modern aviation were heroes. They get the same kind of social credit we extend to folks who served overseas in the military. They help all of us.

RISK AVERSION IS REWARD AVERSION.

MORE TECHNOLOGY; MORE PROGRESS

We didn't fly for the entire history of humanity, and then suddenly we did. **Our only real constraint is physical law.** This is why I don't pay much attention to people claiming something is impossible based solely on past failure. Things change, tech advances, and the mythical Icarus is succeeded by the very real Wrights.

Often, technological breakthroughs are presented in movies as an Icarus-style story, with an old, outdated moral: "Oh, they were so arrogant with their technology. They flew too close to the sun, and their wings melted, and they fell back to the earth. They should not have been so arrogant as to think they could aim so high."

That's the implication of *Jurassic Park*, *The Terminator*, and *Black Mirror*. All the bad things that happen are about the hubris of the scientists and blah, blah, blah. The movie *Limitless* is about a guy who finds a wonder drug that unlocks the use of our fullest intelligence. There are side effects, but the movie is so refreshing because, at the end, the guy works out the bugs. With his super intelligence, he's able to figure out the better version of the pill. That's how it works in real life.

We aren't like Icarus. We had some crashes, but we figured out how to have safe, reliable planes stay up in the sky. We engineered the failures away.

We figured out a way around the seemingly un-figure-out-able. Believing the next problem is solvable is a fundamental tenet of the philosophy of technology.

> If you haven't studied something in depth, your mental model of it often implicitly reduces to a few scenes from a Hollywood movie.

Technology is the driving force of history. The entire premise of science fiction is that some new scientific invention has changed the world. We only seem to understand this in the context of a movie (where the changes are often for the worse and happen in fast-forward montages), but not in the context of the world today (where the changes are often for the better and happen one day at a time).

Put another way, science and technology are not the newspaper headlines of each day; politics and crime are—even if the former is where most of our attention should be.

Through history, regimes rise and fall, but technology is (so far!) up and to the right. What distinguishes man from ape is technological progress. The more things that can get done without you thinking about them, the more civilizational progress there has been.

When I hit the Enter key to send an email, many, many things happen. I depress the key, the capacitor changes when I hit that key, the wireless keyboard has Bluetooth to send it to the laptop, the laptop captures that event and turns it into packets, and so on. Five hundred things are happening, and you're not thinking about any of those things. Progress is abstraction.

The issue that stems from abstraction is people get alienated from complexity and start to believe things are easy. That's just humans being humans. Actually, putting all those things behind an easy interface is ridiculously hard. It's really, really, really hard to do. It's really hard to make something easy.

We really should be in the middle of a golden age of productivity. Within living memory, computers did not exist. Photocopiers did not exist. *Backspace* did not exist. You had to write everything by hand. Not long ago, you couldn't search your documents, let alone sort them, back them up, look things up, copy/paste, email, or undo. You had to type everything on a typewriter!

If you're doing information work, relative to your ancestors who worked with papyrus, paper, or typewriters, you are a golden god surfing on a sea of electrons. You can make things happen in seconds that would have taken them weeks, if they could do them at all.

Think about the increase in the number of communications per person. We've gone from an occasional letter or phone call to now sending data with every keystroke.

Lots of people mistake the value of new technologies. Things that initially seem frivolous become important down the line. Video games led to 3D graphics, now leading to virtual reality. Social networking led to services like Lyft. Twitter started as breakfast updates, and now it's used for revolutions and breaking news. Those things are not as trivial as people think.

THE IMPACT OF TECHNOLOGY

> We haven't made the emotional case for technology.
>
> The assumption behind sci-fi like *Black Mirror* is that the present is okay, but technology could make the future dystopian.
>
> But perhaps the present is dystopian and technology is our only hope for a positive future.

TECHNOLOGY LOWERS PRICES

Prices are up in education, healthcare, and real estate, but they're down in computers and telecommunications. In every area technology touches, the price decreases.

Everybody becomes more equal because they have the same iPhone or Android phone experience. They've got the same Google, Wikipedia, GitHub—anything that is digital.

The consumer economy actually creates a form of equality. At a massive, massive scale, you produce the same product for everybody. There's not that much difference between a top-end smartphone and a low-end one.

Every area the government touches sees prices inflate. That's due to regulations or subsidies, which impairs the increases of labor productivity from technology.

For example, in medicine, a doctor is required to be in the loop for any diagnostic decisions, even if artificial intelligence can do it better than 99 percent of doctors. (And 99 percent is just in early experiments. Once you get the AI into production with all the data, it will become better than every doctor.)

Maybe we have a medical doctor supervising it so it's not just a program running by itself without any supervision. But right now we aren't allowed to automate the doctor because of regulations and subsidies.

A subsidy is similar to a regulation because it casts a particular way of doing things into stone. That's why we still have yellow school buses and number two pencils. These decisions are set in budget appropriations, locked in, and then they become lagging aspects of the system.

Law, medicine, education, finance, real estate...all of these are lagging areas that are regulated or subsidized. Technology has partially reformed them, but not fully. Now, they're just relics being dragged into the future.

There is obviously value to tradition. People say something is "Lindy" to mean it's been proven by the test of time, or existed for a long time. But, of course, there's a tension between tradition and innovation. Going to the moon wasn't Lindy; it was just awesome. This is a tension within humanity itself.

Technology changes microeconomic leverage. It expands the range of options available to each person:

→ Accept ignorance vs. search Google
→ Accept a broadcast vs. reply on social media
→ Accept fiat vs. buy Bitcoin

You may want to know, talk back, or opt out. Now you can.

> Technology is the driving force of history.
>
> It lies upstream of culture, and thus upstream of politics.

A technological determinist view of history is surprisingly rare. From this view, much of history is not as much about the eternal rights of man as about the newest features of machines.

Mapmaking technologies enabled the creation of accurate maps. We take this for granted today, but without good maps, there were no explicit borders, only a gradual diminishing of the power of one sovereign as its territory bled into another.

In theory, the state was meant to be an innovation in violence reduction. You stay in your territory; I stay in mine. Clear sovereigns would keep domestic order, and the principle of national sovereignty would deter aggression from abroad. It didn't entirely work out like that, of course. Both intrastate and interstate conflict still occurred. But it may have been preferable to the preceding era of fuzzy-bordered empires and sovereign conflicts.

Feudalism was enforced by knights on horseback in shining armor with heavy swords; guns changed that. Guns reduced the importance of physical inequality. Any man (or importantly, woman) with a gun could kill any other man, even if the shooter was old and frail and the shootee was Sir Lancelot himself.

Guns destabilized the feudal hierarchy; a strong right arm was suddenly worth less than a strong left brain, because the technology and supply chain to produce muskets was suddenly critical. The gun helped catalyze the transition from feudal hierarchy to nationalist republic and enabled the "republican" ideals of the American and French Revolutions to thrive.

Today, we're on phones and computers. Whether it's politics or wars, it starts with the device.

Our mental picture of war is what we see on the History Channel. But it's actually going to look like what we've seen online over the last twenty years, which is terrorism, social media, memes, hacks, cancellation, deplatforming, unbanking, and assassination. That's what conflict looks like in the networked age.

There's both a good and bad aspect to this. It's probably less destructive to property and lives than missiles and nuclear warheads; but it's also worse because the battlefront is both everywhere and nowhere.

To be against technology is to be on the wrong side of history. You can't put the genie back in the bottle. You won't take away voices newly gained by billions.

Technological innovation drives moral innovation. Human nature may be roughly constant, but technology is not. New technology leads to the re-evaluation of existing moral principles and, sometimes, to new ones.

"Freedom of speech" meant one thing in 1776, something else during the era of highly centralized mass media, and something different again in an era when every type of data is transmitted in speech-like digital symbols over the internet.

Moral innovation also drives technological innovation. Once believing in a heliocentric (sun-centered) model of the solar system was no longer considered morally evil, people developed more accurate star charts. In the fullness of time, that led to oceanic navigation, satellites, and space travel.

> Technology determines which fringe ideas have become newly feasible and what elements of current consensus have become suddenly obsolete.

There is so much emerging tech to be excited about: Bitcoin, Ethereum, and crypto in general; startup cities; reversing aging; brain-machine interfaces; transhumanism; robotics; digital nomadism; AI-assisted content creation, including AI video and decentralized video; virtual reality as a replacement for offices; augmented reality for productivity; telemedicine; personal genomics; CRISPR; health tracking; pure biomedicine as well as consumer biomedicine, which overlaps with quantified self. 3D printing in metals is a little more speculative, but I think that's getting better quietly. Pseudonymity aided by crypto and AI voices and faces is also emerging. I think we'll build an entire pseudonymous economy.

I have to remind myself that these things are still new to 99 percent of the population. The way to calibrate this is to ask the average person, "What are the top five 3D printers?" or "What are the top five drones?" Most people can't go into the full list. Maybe they can name one or two, but they can't tell you all the innovation that's happening, so it's still early in that space.

> The incredible thing many people don't get? Technology is just getting started. We're only at the base of the exponential.

> What is politically feasible is a function of what is technologically feasible.

The design space for legitimate governments is larger than one might think. The key ingredient is ongoing consent, more than a particular form of government.

Every political idea has been out there since antiquity. What waxes and wanes is the technological feasibility of ideas. Technology is now making all those impractical libertarian ideas (panarchy, polycentric law, Tiebout sorting) not just practical but inevitable.

A new idea doesn't need a consensus to have a chance. It just needs to not have too strong a consensus *against* it. A minimum alignment is necessary, a set of beliefs you need to agree on with someone, to put everything else aside and move forward on a common goal.

Any mayor or governor can pick a technology, draw a line through old laws, and put the word out to technologists. There are hundreds of countries with thousands of mayors. For any new technology, one of them will be first. Each new technology provides a new path to rapidly becoming a world city.

> Democrats need to learn experts aren't always right.
>
> Republicans need to learn experts aren't always wrong.
>
> Libertarians need to learn that a state can succeed.
>
> Progressives need to learn that a state can fail.

I truly believe in complying with every law, because you do have a gun to your head. But compliance is not submission. You can work to change the laws. Do everything you can within the law to alter the law.

Google founder and computer scientist Larry Page said any law more than fifty years old has to be re-examined. Any law written before the internet needs to get re-examined, or it's going to collapse. Cryptocurrency is going to cause the same situation.

Today we have ninety-year-old laws wielded by seventy-year-old people to prevent twenty-somethings from using twenty-first century technology.

At the end of the day, you sometimes need to work with governments. But you should always put your trust in technology over politicians because technology is what works no matter what politician is in office.

As states lose trust, their soft power declines. Less deference to the state means less voluntary compliance. Then, only hard power is left. The more states use hard power (coercion), the less soft power (persuasion) they have. Which means yet more use of hard power. It's a negative feedback loop.

> Government is not going to limit itself. Only technology can limit it.

> Society, driven by technology, goes through cycles of centralization and decentralization.
>
> The decentralization phase approaches.

One of the most interesting things I've learned is how much the twentieth century was the product of centralizing technologies: centralized broadcast media (movies, news, radio) as well as centralized production (factories) of centralized armies (tanks, aircraft, nukes), which were all run by extremely powerful centralized states. It can be said the twentieth century was the centralized century.

Using our technological determinist perspective, we'd say it was difficult to coordinate California with New York in the 1800s, necessitating some degree of independence. This changed in the 20th century, when one face could now be broadcast to millions. The cult of personality and centralized coordination of people enabled total war. One person, even if right, could not stand against many. To disagree with the whims of the crowd meant death in many countries for many decades.

Technology started enabling decentralization with the personal computer in the late '70s, then with the internet in 1991, and now with Bitcoin. The twenty-first century may be in many ways opposite of the twentieth.

The year 1950 was peak centralization. In 1950, you had one telephone company, two superpowers, and three television stations: AT&T; the US and USSR; and ABC, CBS, and NBC. Everything was super, super, super centralized. There were just a few choke points in everything, with very little choice. Everything was homogenized. Everybody was watching the same shows on television. Society was all flattened out and smoothed out.

As you go backward and forward, things start getting more decentralized. Moving forward, you get cable television, the internet, blogs, social media, and cryptocurrency. One of the really fascinating things is, when going backward in time, it's as if we're rewinding the tape with certain events from the past, now appearing in the future, but out of order.

This is just one interesting theory: our future is our past.

It's not so much that decentralization is a panacea. It's that when you are over-centralized, you decentralize. And then, if people over-decentralize, they recentralize—but around new hubs each time.

So it's bundling, unbundling, then rebundling.

Decentralization doesn't mean an absence of leadership. It means a choice of many leaders. Crypto has allowed millions of people to partially exit their existing financial and political systems for large-scale experiments in self-governance and self-determination...even if not all of them have realized this yet. Decentralization restores the consent of the governed.

Why does decentralization win in the long run? With millions of developers and billions of phones, the internet is now essential for daily life, and crypto is built to be international, private, and monetizable without a central entity. It's hard to stop these decentralizing technologies.

You can summon the CEO of Facebook to Congress. You can't summon the "CEO of email" to Congress. There is no CEO. That's where this is all going.

Censorship incentivizes decentralization.

The state has six hours of compulsory education per day for kids. What's interesting is the internet is getting a lot of those hours, taking them away from the state. Kids are plugged into their laptops, iPads, and iPhones, self-educating instead of having compulsory state education.

An interesting thing is happening when kids are plugged into a different network, not the state-approved network, during their nascent years. They're plugged into their own communities and subcultures. The state today has a lot less control over kids as they're growing up.

If you go all the way back to why Bismarck instituted public education, you'll learn it was really to raise children who were "obedient to the state," who were patriots. That acculturation is happening less and less because kids are seeing people who have different ideologies at a much younger age, with a lot of interesting medium-term consequences.

Downsides are obvious. You have kids who are less able to make eye contact because they're staring at a screen all day. Literally, maybe, their eyes physically can't focus at medium distance as much anymore. It's harder for kids to focus on books and to do deep reading because they're constantly distracted by notifications.

The upsides, of course, are they have access to the Library of Alexandria for free any time. If they're really good at math or computer science or have any other interest, they can find like-minded communities. They're not forced into twelve years of one-size-fits-all quasi-jail at modern American public schools. Instead, they can self-educate, self-advance, and level up. I think lots of kids are going to be remote working at a much earlier age. We certainly will have 20-something billionaires. We'll probably have a teenage billionaire soon, if we haven't already had one.

On balance, I think it's probably positive on the net, though we want to figure out some way to ameliorate those downsides.

> Everything technology is doing means more upside, more downside. That's my one-liner for the future: more upside, more downside.

OUR DIGITAL FUTURE

PHYSICAL, THEN DIGITAL, THEN NATIVE DIGITAL

We went from pieces of paper to a scanner/printer/fax to purely digital files that have no physical origin. We may go from movies to computer-generated imagery (CGI) in movies to entirely computer-generated videos, never originally filmed with human beings offline. We may go from physical cash to an online bank balance to cryptocurrency, which is inherently digital.

This is a useful progression to think through for many areas because you can see inherently digital versions often don't exist yet. The last twenty years has just been taking our existing offline versions of things and uploading them to the cloud.

As the fundamental medium changes, the form changes. Search engines and social networks are digital-native concepts that couldn't exist offline. There are many other concepts where the digital-native and crypto-native equivalents are yet to exist. What is a crypto-native equivalent of a diploma? What does crypto art look like? What does fundamentally digital login and identity look like? All these are coming.

Similarly, everybody is talking about machine learning and AI in the last few years as if it's a new thing. That technology was being developed at Stanford fifteen years ago. Innovations take time to evolve and diffuse out to the public.

USAIN BOLT CAN RUN 2X FASTER THAN MOST PEOPLE.
ONE ALGORITHM CAN RUN 1,000 TIMES FASTER THAN ANOTHER.
SCALES DIFFER IN SOFTWARE.

THE BLOCKCHAIN DISRUPTION

Crypto will disrupt tech, just like tech disrupted everything else. There is overlap, but crypto is really a different sector down to the base level of how organizations are formed, monetized, and exited. Like the cloud and mobile transitions, it will take decades to fully play out.

Living through this incredible bottom-up revolution shows what one person with a computer can do. Satoshi Nakamoto changed the world's financial system, established a new digital reserve currency, and shifted the thinking of the Davos elite with just a keyboard and the right ideas.

> I would be far more bearish on the future if Bitcoin didn't exist.

The terms "emoney" and "digital currency" are vastly better than "cryptocurrency" for quickly conveying what crypto is about. Just as email took the stamp away from mail, emoney holds the promise of eliminating the transaction fee.

If the internet was programmable communication, crypto is programmable money. Before the internet, you needed a deal with a telecom company to deploy information-transferring code. Before Bitcoin, you needed a deal with a bank to deploy value-transferring code.

New types of transactions are enabled by cryptocurrency: the very small, the very large, the very fast, the very automated, and/or the very international.

Those saying, "Crypto is just another asset class" sound like those who said, "The internet is just another media outlet." They didn't understand programmability, permissionless-ness, or peer-to-peer, and they overestimated the robustness of legacy institutions. History repeats with crypto.

Crypto is more than an asset class because it transforms the custody, trading, issuance, governance, and programmability of anything scarce. It's a new financial system, not just some ticker symbols.

The internet subsumed TV, radio, newspapers, movies, *and* created new kinds of media. Crypto likewise will subsume stocks, bonds, commodities, *and* create new kinds of assets.

Crypto is about digital property rights. By default, you should own your social media account. A platform that can seize it without due process is like a bank that can seize your money at will. Blockchains today protect you against the banks and tomorrow will protect you against social media platforms.

> Blockchains provide the technical foundation for a new digital theory of property rights.

People will go from being internet influencers to crypto creators. The difference is crypto creators have property rights on their content. If you don't own private keys to something, you don't really own it. Like your social media account—you have conditional access to something that could get taken away.

When Trump got deplatformed from Twitter, whatever else you think about that, future historians will look at that as a moment "the most powerful man in the world wasn't even the most powerful man in his own country." It showed that your social media account is not yours.

To truly be a creator, you have to be a crypto creator, not an internet influencer. The gap between them is the gap of digital property rights. And that gap is huge.

This is a huge unlock for billions of people on social media. Three billion people are on Facebook, yet nobody controls any digital property rights. Your social media is not just your tweets or your posts—it is your relationship to your friends and followers. It is your ability to earn money without You-Tube taking a big cut of the revenue, or just turning it off. Why should this gigantic corporation be able to silence you or seize your assets at will?

It might take ten to twenty years, but as blockchains scale, every centralized service can become a decentralized protocol. Times have changed, and the economic terms of the agreement are changing. People are realizing they're not in control and they're not getting a cut.

Crypto is a spinal transplant for the tech industry.

On disk → Online → On-chain. On-chain is like the third level of deployment. Files that only you care about stay on your local disk. Files that are important to others get put online. And files that are *really* important to others will get put on the blockchain.

When you put information online, you get distribution, sharing, collaboration, etc. When you put it on-chain, you get immutability, verifiability, monetization, etc. On-chain is not suitable for everything, just like you don't put everything online. Putting something on-chain is a stronger version of putting it online. It lessens the impacts of link rot, stealth editing, downtime, format obsolescence, firewalls, and many related issues.

Blockchains also enable distributed consensus on questions like: Who wrote this? Who signed this? When did they sign it? What did they sign?

Over the next decade, financiers and engineers will use on-chain data more and more, because it's the input to every smart contract...which is the basis for every investment decision in the cryptoeconomy...which becomes an ever larger share of the global economy. Because all value becomes digital, the entire economy will eventually become the cryptoeconomy.

> The last era was big data. The next era is verifiable data.

TECHNOLOGY TO CREATE ALIGNMENT

The concept of alignment is fundamental. Alignment is critical to the communities and structures we want to build in the future. I think alignment has to be quantifiable. Crypto is a technology for creating alignment.

One thing people don't get yet is that crypto is not just the next Wall Street. It's also the next Silicon Valley. Decentralized social networks are built there already.

Even less obviously, crypto is the next Yale Law, Columbia School of Journalism, and Kennedy School of Government. Why? Because Yale Law will get replaced by smart contracts. Columbia School of Journalism will get replaced by crypto event feeds.

Kennedy School of Government will get replaced because the next Heads of State actually will be Heads of Networks. The people who found and run these gigantic crypto networks, sometimes in the billions or trillions of dollars, will be like Fed Chairs of a state, if not a country.

They've gotten there by founding something. These are founders who are aligned with their people, people who have all opted-in to be part of their networks. Quantifiable alignment is the ethical way to ensure leaders help the whole population.

What if there's an "align" movement? Where all the other peace-loving peoples of the world are able to effectively align behind crypto protocols that give genuine rule of law? Such protocols would provide for freedom of speech and freedom of contract, with contracts that work across borders so you know you're not going to be cheated. You would have your counter-part's international trade reputation.

For education, we could have an institution the equivalent of Harvard on-chain with crypto credentials, but one that doesn't have fees. It wouldn't be exclusive in the same way, but it would be more meritocratic.

> Crypto allows free markets without corporations.

Bitcoin at $100B is an industry. Bitcoin at $1T is a world power. Bitcoin at $10T would be the global government that so many have predicted, just in very different form. If Bitcoin can truly make it to $10T and stay there, it would constrain all the nations of the world.

A company can issue new shares to promote corporate growth, but if it issues too many, investors hold cash instead. A nation can print more cash to promote economic growth, but if it prints too much, investors hold Bitcoin instead.

Why trust Bitcoin? You can find out who wrote every line of the codebase and when, where, and why. This is significantly more transparent than many other finance systems we work with on a daily basis.

The long-term impact of crypto may make finance fundamen-tally less profitable. The existing financial system has ATM fees, overdraft fees, wire transfer fees, origination fees, and fees of every kind at the retail level and investment level.

I think it's interesting to make a table of every fee in finance and ask which of them are actually going to be around in twenty years. How much of the profit will get pushed out of finance? I can imagine we will treat finance almost like a communications network.

Then we will have more profit for people who are actually building businesses and doing things of value. It is possible fortunes in the future are made only by funding or building startups. It will take decades to play out, but the economic logic of crypto-versus-financial-services is similar to internet-versus-telecom.

> By 2040, everyone under 30 will have never known a world without Bitcoin. It may as well be gold. That's the long-term case for replacement.

THE DIGITAL FRONTIER

In 1890, the physical frontier closed. In 1991, a virtual frontier opened. The major difference with this virtual frontier: anyone with a keyboard can build on it, not just Americans. Indeed, the majority are non-American.

Over twenty years, the eyes and ears of hundreds of millions of people have migrated from pieces of paper to mobile programmable screens. People's bodies may be in various nations or countries, but their minds are elsewhere—online, with communities of shared interests and beliefs.

One thesis is these mental migrations online will ultimately cause offline physical migrations. The intermediate form is likely to be virtual worlds.

In theory, social networks like Six Degrees existed before Twitter or Facebook. In practice, without profile photos, there was no human connection. Similarly, people don't yet viscerally feel the size of online crowds. Once millions have VR headsets, that will change.

A large number of people already spend more time looking at a laptop or phone than doing any other activity. The smartphone in particular caused a qualitative jump in percent of time spent online. VR will likely cause a comparable jump.

Even without VR headsets, we can envision things. First, one can imagine highly interactive storefronts that gain the searchability and convenience of online shopping. People love malls. Put those in VR and we gain teleporting between points, search, instant checkout, and worldwide payments with crypto. Second, we can imagine taking any online forum and putting it in VR. For example, car aficionados could discuss interactive VR models of favorite cars.

To generalize: with VR, the metaphor of "building" on a frontier becomes more real. We can build structures that combine online and offline features.

Digital globalist, physical localist.

Imagine we divide physical America from digital America. Seen from this axis, much of the physical world is malfunctioning. Meanwhile, people migrate to the digital world because things "just work" there. Given the alternative, most pick the digital alternative.

Over the last few decades, a significant part of the value of being physically present in America has been digitized. COVID-19 and remote work accelerated digital life and further reduced the value of the physical. The cloud is becoming primary, the land secondary.

Consider the following choices:

1. physical America + digital America
2. physical America only, but no internet
3. digital America only, but not physically in the US

My thesis: more people would rank 3 above 2 today. Which means much of the US value proposition has moved to the cloud. This is a very recent phenomenon. In 1990, for example, you couldn't "live on the internet." It was maybe barely doable in some US regions in the year 2000 and was still hard in 2010. Now digital America is everywhere, because the internet is everywhere.

> With the internet, one can now stand against infinity. For good or ill, we're going to see many more like Snowden, Assange, Wilson, and Nakamoto.

ALL VALUE BECOMES DIGITAL

All wealth becomes digital. Everything becomes a set of digital instructions. A printer or robot then executes those instructions to affect the real world. Amazon Prime, drop shipping, food delivery, ride-sharing...all of them involve a digital frontend and a human backend.

Over time, more pieces are getting automated, so the backend becomes digital too. AI (in general) and virtual influencers (specifically) are obvious examples of this trend, where the human backend is no longer as necessary.

> Even when the goods themselves can't be digitized, the interfaces to them will be.

If you think about what comes *after* what comes next...you'll see that just being good at building software may be sufficient by 2050, because a lot of physical production will be automated through robotics.

All property will become digital because much of the physical world will become printing. Obviously, you can print out a digital document on a piece of paper today. But think about a supply chain of robots delivering food to your door. We are already doing some autonomous food prep. For delivery, we have autonomous cars or sidewalk delivery robots. You can imagine the whole food creation and delivery process being fully automated, all robots—an electromechanical process that has no human intervention. It would be just like printing something out.

I think in the future, most value will be created online, and you'll print it out by invoking robotics. Robotics is sort of happening in our peripheral vision now. In the 2020s, we're going to see more actual robots in the field. That's going to come pretty quickly, because once a robot can do something, you've turned labor into capital.

All labor can become capital. When that happens, being really good at engineering just gets higher and higher and higher leverage. The robotic world I just described is not only for food delivery. The same dynamic will exist in warfare, agriculture, and manufacturing. Being really good at software is going to keep earning compounding returns. That's important.

I'm increasingly thinking of the physical world as a printout of digital wealth. Ask yourself: what can hitting a button do? In 2010, one button could print a PDF. In 2020, one button can deliver any item. In 2030, maybe one button can build anything.

In crypto, much of the labor in the financial system is being automated with smart contracts and digital signatures. Because all wealth goes digital, all wealth will go crypto over the next few decades—not just currencies, loans, stocks, commodities, art, and video game items, but every type of human wealth. It all will become natively digital, the input to a robotic "printer."

OUR PHYSICAL FUTURE

AUTOMATION DELIVERS ABUNDANCE

Drones are going to be a very big deal. There are different kinds of drones, not just flying drones. There are swimming drones and walking drones and so on. Think about how drones could affect construction.

Drones won't be just autonomous. You will be able to teleport into a drone and control something on the other side of the world. Maybe you put it in autonomous mode to walk to a destination. You wake up to find it has arrived at the destination; now you can take over for more precise control.

An interesting movie called *Surrogates* explores what a really big drone/telepresence future would look like. In the movie, people never leave their homes. Instead, they just connect into a really good-looking drone/telepresent version of themselves and walk around in that. If they're hit by cars, it doesn't matter because they can just create new drones and rejuvenate. The impact of drones is very, very underrated.

> Every human-to-human interface replaced with a human-to-machine interface reduces the relative importance of social status versus technical competence.

I've often thought that the most fundamental way to price things might be energy, measured in joules. How much energy did it take to assemble my phone, to pull the materials out of the ground and shape them into that configuration?

Knowing the joules required to build something would give us a ratio-scale measure of the cost of production. This "true" price system would let us disentangle factors like inflation and subsidies from the physical cost of manufacturing. If it cost 1,000 joules of energy to produce something in 1950s America but one hundred joules today, that's much better. You could get into the guts of the manufacturing to find the exact spot where the improvement occurred. (Big jumps would be due to something like the Haber process.)

The trickiest part may be pricing human labor. Two people may both consume a sandwich's worth of energy but have different skills. It makes sense to start with joule-based pricing for already automated processes where physical goods are manufactured in "steady state" at scale.

The defining industrial innovation of the twentieth century was the assembly line. For the twenty-first, it may be industrial robotics. With industrial robotics, management becomes code running automation.

Factories have had robots for quite a while, but advances in robotics have made it possible to automate whole facilities. Even tasks that currently require extreme manual dexterity will soon be done by robot hands.

This will have significant consequences. Among other things, by turning management into code, management now becomes tangible. Soon, managers of an assembly line can replace employee training with scriptable machine images, replace architectural diagrams for assembly line configurations, and think in terms of protocols rather than internal memos.

Communication tasks by the manager now become programs recorded in git logs and database entries. The manager blends into the worker, and the assembly line morphs into a robotic factory scripted by the manager's instructions in code.

This means far fewer workers, which means far fewer other constraints. For better or for worse, no employment law provisions apply to robots. Robots have no hourly restrictions, minimum wage laws, collective bargaining agreements, or decommissioning restrictions. OSHA's power over the workplace plummets when there are no workers.

This scenario is alarming, not just to the already embattled US factory worker, but to workers at Chinese companies like Foxconn who may be replaced by robots. As this technological trend accelerates, the capital requirements to produce a product will decline precipitously. To run a small robotic factory could be like running your own data center, well within reach of the individual entrepreneur.

> Universal healthcare is not enough. We need eternal life.

We don't know what's going on inside our bodies. We don't know what's going on subcutaneously, under the skin. We know what's going on in Bangalore or Budapest, but not in our bodies. We have information from the other side of the world, but not something a few inches away. This lack of knowledge is actually an astounding blank spot on the map.

Back in the 1990s, we had the concept of getting lost. You don't get lost anymore. With GPS, you always know your location. In the future, you will always know your internal state.

Studying the different cultures of healthcare versus fitness is instructive. They are almost opposites in terms of individual versus institutional responsibility.

We view healthcare as an institutional responsibility, yet a doctor is with you for only thirty minutes, and you are with your body all of the time. If you bring a doctor data from the internet, you are either right (and undermining them) or wrong (and ignorant). Either way, self-care is disincentivized. Yet, even very competent doctors can't substitute for self-care.

This is interesting, because we accept we are personally responsible for our fitness. A personal trainer is viewed as a helper at most.

We may find self-care based on self-measurement, personal genomics, and fitness is the actual wonder drug. Fitness is a good entry point for self-care, with a long-term option to combine your individual personal data with broad clinical data.

Self-measurement isn't "n=1" science (small sample size); it is "t=infinity" science (long timeframe). This yields unprecedented personal health data. Smart food companies will use this data to deliver data-driven personalized nutrition.

Your body, your choice. If you can legally skydive or bungee jump, if you can serve in the military and risk life and limb, you should be able to take arbitrary risks with your own health. That means we need expanded rights to try medicines and treatments and new pathways outside the FDA, at home and abroad. Certainly experimenting medically is more socially beneficial than bungee jumping or skydiving, which is risk without reward.

> Self-measurement may ultimately resolve all nutrition controversies.

When you eat something, it is literally incorporated into your body. If society were smarter about this, you might be able to track it. When you eat a piece of chicken or lettuce, where are those lipids, those carbohydrates, those proteins incorporated exactly? Do they go to your eyes? Are they all diffused? Do they gravitate toward particular places?

You are made of what you eat. Your body is being reconstructed by these foods. Interesting studies are trying to track where various foods end up deposited. This intersects with genetics and what we know about biochemistry and metabolism in the fields of pharmacogenomics and nutrigenomics, which is the response of your body to what you consume. For example, you individually might be a fast or slow metabolizer of caffeine or alcohol.

> It's interesting to think about things discussed informally that will become computable objects. "I feel sick" is a big one.

Future historians may note this was the era of sugar, caffeine, opioids, and social media, just like previous eras were in part driven by nicotine and alcohol. Maybe there's always a dominant drug of the age, even if we don't see it.

Over the last fifty to sixty years, restaurant culture has become more and more mainstream. We've gone from having family-cooked meals, where the people who were our food providers were also our healthcare providers, to outsourcing all nutrition to capitalist entities who are not aligned with us.

That's why we have sugary, unhealthy foods. They are engineered to be delicious to get you to eat more and buy huge portion sizes. Then you suffer later with diabetes or metabolic disorders. Look up the obesity epidemic. It's frightening because it actually looks like a true epidemic.

A failing restaurant will start throwing sugar and other additives into its food because people respond to those things. But it's a short-term, unbalanced optimization.

It's like when Coca-Cola put cocaine in the cola. Today, we say, "Wow, that's so bad." But when, in recent years, people added fruit syrup to yogurt, we say, "Wow, now it's selling!" In the future, when everybody has continuous glucose monitors, we will actually see the blood sugar spikes we've been experiencing.

Then, we will see this time period (when people had sugar for breakfast and sugar for lunch, when kids were eating sugar for a snack, and when sugar was in everything) as similar to the time when drugs were laced into consumer products.

The overabundance of sugar is why people are so fat now. It's why diabetes is such an epidemic. Sugar starts messing up your gut microbiome and causes other issues. It's very difficult to escape, like secondhand smoke. It's in almost everything. You have to really try to not eat sugar.

It's funny to notice the most nutritious foods—lettuce, tomatoes, fruits, etc.—don't have nutrition facts on them. That's because a little bit of a chemistry experiment has to occur to require complex nutrition facts.

> It would be interesting if diet could reduce the need for sleep. Precedent: modern diets permanently increased our height.

Think about those "I took a picture of myself every day for three years" videos. Could a simple video selfie be a diagnostic tool for health tracking? The key is determining how many health signals you can estimate from a high-definition video of your face taken every day: heart rate, jaundice, BMI, and probably many more.

We can call this device a "magic mirror." Look at it in the morning, and it says, "You look sick" and tells you why. Correlating the magic mirror video with other self-measurement data (like nutrition and fitness trackers) could give persuasive demos: "If you do this, you will look like this."

Essentially, a magic mirror could make personalized "before/ after" examples to visually demonstrate the effects of fitness and diet changes on your health and appearance.

NOT LIFE EXTENSION, YOUTH EXTENSION

Ending death should be the highest priority of technology. We now know that reversing aging may be technically achievable.

When you deal with mechanical things like cars, you can calculate a failure rate for each part. Some cars are lucky and never experience any of those failures. One out of ten thousand cars may make it fifty years or one hundred years without being repaired, because the errors don't accumulate. By random chance, a car might be able to last a long time.

Humans aren't like that. There is a hard drop-off at 120 years old. If humans broke down like cars, some humans would live to a thousand. Instead, what happens is a predictable and coordinated process where people kind of go gray and get fat in similar ways as they age. Now, there's a lot of evidence this is actually a triggered and coordinated event. Just like you're genetically wired to grow from a baby into an adult, you're genetically wired to die. Maybe we can unwire that. In fact, folks are working on it now.

Get life extension or die tryin'.

A better term might be "youth extension." Many people think life extension would just mean more years as a senior citizen. But if we could keep you at twenty-something from a physiological standpoint, or even get you back there, that would be very different.

When I say, "I want life extension," some people who support universal healthcare reply, "That's impractical. We can't do that." They're missing the point. Are we trying to extend the end of somebody's life from seventy-five to seventy-eight years? Or is the goal to proactively increase quantity and quality of life for everybody?

The moral is clear: if you're against life extension, you want us to die. We can win that moral battle; people have to concede. If you're for universal healthcare, you better be for life extension research and technologies.

There has been tremendous progress in the molecular biology of aging in the last decade. Professor Sinclair of Harvard Medical School has a great line: "Aging may be a reversible condition, if it is caught early." Eventually, we'll want to measure methylation or similar biomarkers for aging as frequently as possible. You might actually detect months where you are aging faster or slower.

> Longevity has the potential to be to traditional medicine what crypto is to traditional finance. It changes the terms of the debate.

Longevity rejects the most fundamental premise of the legacy medical system—that death is inevitable and arguably desirable—and branches the entire biomedical tech stack in a new direction. Making life-extension tech widely accessible is important for ethical reasons and to build the largest possible coalition of support.

We should prioritize this because life extension makes everything relatively cheaper. If a purchase used to cost you $100 and now costs you $1, that purchase takes 100x less time from your life because your working life produced that $100 or $1 by trading your time. Rather than spending, say, one hundred minutes of your life, you spent one minute. Life extension, or reversing aging, is the ultimate scarcity reduction. It gives everybody lots of time.

Life extension should be technically feasible now. That's the thing people don't get yet. Reversing aging is possible. It's starting to happen now in mice.

There is almost nobody who gets older and enjoys it, right? Life extension products would be some of the most popular products ever.

TRANSHUMANISM: SELF-IMPROVEMENT WITH TECHNOLOGY

The goal of transhumanism is simply to become the absolute best version of yourself. I think all of tech will be focused on it in five to ten years.

Transhumanism is human self-improvement with technology. This is a very wide set of things. Transhumanism encompasses self-measurement, external devices (like phones, watches, glasses, earbuds, contacts), body modifications, super-soldier serums (check out myostatin null), brain-machine interfaces (like neuralink), nootropics and other cognition-enhancing drugs (like in the movie *Limitless*), genetic modifications with CRISPR for genetic diseases, and AI-augmented human capabilities (bionics, telepresence). It's basically a suite of technologies to power up humans.

If we were to deliver just some of these and scale to millions of people, it would be huge. That's like the creation of eyeglasses times 1,000. However, transhumanism has gotten pushback from people who are afraid of any change for humanity, whether a change is good or bad.

My approach is "optimismalism;" that is, improving things in an objective way, neither using too much technology nor too little. You can have too much fire, and you can have too little fire. We want to use just enough fire to warm us and cook food—not so little that we freeze, and not so much we burn down the house.

Humans have been living with technology in this way forever. Fire arguably made us human. Richard Wrangham's book *Catching Fire* describes how the invention of fire allowed humans to outsource some of our metabolism to the fire and allocate more scarce calories for brain development. This relaxed an evolutionary constraint, which made us smarter and more human. We've been coevolving with technology for a very, very long time, throughout evolutionary timescales. Technology is actually what makes us human. It's what distinguishes man from animal.

> If you distill how I think about the world, it's how to level up as an individual, then as a group, and then for humanity as a whole.

The future I envision is much better than how we live today. How much better? Think of how much better we are now than starving medieval peasants or slaves building the pyramids. Future humans will look at today's living standard the way we look at those living conditions. **These leaps in progress can continue.**

We can ascend. Humans expanded out of Africa to the rest of the world. Oceanic navigation let us cross oceans. When we created submarines, we could go underwater. After inventing airplanes, we could fly. That's the transhumanism of the past. Those machines all added to human capabilities.

Our current constraints will fall away too. We can expand to the stars. We can live underwater. What else comes next?

PART II

TRUTH

Many things that are true are unpopular;

many things that are popular are untrue.

THE TYPES OF TRUTH

You're pursuing truth, health, and wealth, in that order. That's actually the right priority order. For example, you'd never want to do something that's untrue to make money or sacrifice your long-term health for wealth. Learn to determine what is true. Pursue health because, without that, you have really nothing else. Then wealth is important, but it's third—though it's important to have that third.

> Most people do social diligence; only a few do technical diligence.

Is something true if others think it's true? Or is it true regardless of what people think?

Distinguishing social consensus from truth is really important because they're not the same. Often we will say, "Oh, that is true," because there is a social consensus.

You can position facts at two poles: political facts and technical facts. A political fact is true if enough other people believe it to be true; for example, who the president is or where the border of a country is. That's actually a psychological phenomenon. If you can install software to enough people's brains, you can change those truths. That is social consensus.

Then, on the other side, some things are purely technical. A technical fact is the result of an equation or the diameter of a virus under an electron microscope—the result of physical constants. What people think does not change technical truth. Physical facts are independent of any human being. An alien would come to the same conclusions.

> Determining the type of evidence people accept is as important as knowing their incentives.
>
> Some take data, but many accept only popularity.

In theory, we could all just trust computer science. In practice, those who can't code will fall back on trusting in a computer scientist. Decentralizing truth-finding means enabling as many people as possible to do the math themselves.

> If it's not independently reproducible, it's not science.

Our society purports to be based on science. As an academic, I saw how the sausage is really made. Science in the abstract is thought to work like this: there's some phenomenon, you study it, you write a paper, it's peer reviewed, it's published. It's then reported on by news outlets, and then it is used as input for regulation. Regulators then cite the article and, if pressed, the scientific paper backing it up. That is "based on science." That's the assembly line. Seems reasonable.

The problem is when the form and substance of science are mistaken. The *form* of science today is a peer-reviewed journal paper. But the *substance* of science is independent replication.

People confuse genuine science (like Maxwell's equations) with "science" (like a paper that came out last week). Maxwell's equations have had countless trillions of independent replications. The study from last week might not even have shared a public data set. Yet we as a society are supposed to be basing large decisions on this *one* new study?

Many people think "peer review" means "independent replication and confirmation of results." Peer review usually means months of delay while a few folks in your field write an email-length criticism of the paper and ask for more work. Peer review is not a panacea.

Why is independent replication so important? Because science isn't about prestigious people at prestigious universities publishing in prestigious journals echoed by prestigious outlets. Science *is* independent replication.

Some of the people at those prestigious institutions are very intelligent, hard working, and capable of discovering new things and building functional products. But on the whole, the **substitution** of prestige for independent replication isn't serving us well.

Civilization has a ripcord people use when centralized institutions get too ossified. It's called decentralization. Martin Luther used it to argue for the "personal relationship with God," disintermediating the Church. George Washington used it. So did Satoshi Nakamoto.

Given how many hunches have been marketed to us as science, the emphasis on independent replication as the core of science is just such a ripcord. **Only trust as scientific truth what can be independently verified.**

The US research establishment set up in the postwar era is now past its prime. It's an academic jobs program. You see this in things like the h-index, which has the value "h" if you have at least h papers with h citations each. All academics are optimizing their number of citations in high impact journals...but what actually matters in science is not the number of citations. What matters is, once again, independent replication.

And where are the metrics for independent replication? Where are the incentives for it? Not in academic science, where replicating a result isn't considered novel, publishable, or grant-worthy. In fact, replicating a result is often considered hostile. That's why we have the academic replication crisis. Scientific truth was gradually redefined to mean "peer review" rather than "independent replication."

> Imagine if we optimized for number of independent replications over number of citations.

An alternative to the academic research establishment has been bubbling in open source and crypto over the last few decades. Today the circulation of knowledge in science is restricted by the high prices of journals. Many students and researchers cannot afford academic journals and books locked behind paywalls.

The goal of Sci-Hub is to provide free and unrestricted access to all scientific knowledge ever published in journal or book form. I've thought a lot about what a crypto Sci-Hub could look like. It might align incentives so publishers earn money by making all their papers open online. I'm all about aligning incentives if at all possible. If we can, that attacks the problem at its base, because our entire society is based on "science."

Why this regulation? Because science. Why do this? Because science. What is that science? Well, some of it is "science," meaning some dumb study that appeared last week, and some of it is truly fundamental science. We're equating the two when they're not the same.

The way to understand the difference is the number of independent replications. If our data is on-chain, we can start to do that.

> Every statistic is a numerical distillation of a raw data table. Ask for that table.

Science progresses by taking phenomena we think of as non-reproducible (and hence unpredictable), isolating key variables, and turning them into reproducible (and hence predictable) systems. A key example here is understanding that bacteria cause disease.

Science also progresses by improved instrumentation and better recordkeeping. Star charts enabled celestial navigation. Gregor Mendel's careful counting of pea plants led to modern genetics. Johann Balmer's documentation of the exact spacing of hydrogen's emission spectra led to quantum mechanics. Things we believed to be beyond human ken—the stars, the genome, the atom—became things we can comprehend by simply counting them.

I admire Ramanujan. I admire Feynman. These great mathematicians and physicists were able to see things others couldn't. Just by writing down what they observed, they created a huge leap forward.

In entrepreneurship, people often say it's not the idea, it's the execution. But that's for trivial ideas. For great ideas like Maxwell's equations or Newton's laws, the idea itself really does bring us forward.

Sometimes you have the practical phenomenon, but you don't have the theory underneath it. Then that stimulates the advancement of theory to figure out why the thing actually works. For example, people first got steam engines working and only then discovered the thermodynamic theory from that. The practice often leads to the theory rather than vice versa. The limits of our understanding are more of a bug than a feature.

> I see a strong correlation between lack of technical ability and naive trust in social authority. The only true authority is raw data.

TECHNICAL TRUTH

Technical truths—like genetics, math, and biochemistry—are true even if no one believes them to be true. They exist independently of what's in people's brains: What is this virus made of? Will it spread? Can this drug work?

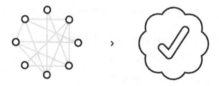

MATHEMATICAL PROOF OVER SOCIAL PROOF.

At first it seems like a trivial or weird statement, but the only thing more prestigious than science is math. They're not normally juxtaposed, but I would say math is greater than science. Math is exact in a sense where science is approximate.

Math is greater than science in another respect, which is independent replications. It's not realistic to expect everybody to have inclined planes, reactors, or chemistry sets at home to replicate experiments for everything. Scientific equipment is expensive. How are people supposed to independently replicate findings? They don't have all the scientific equipment, but you know what they do have? Computers. Computers are mathematical equipment. You can run billions and billions of calculations per second.

So you might not be able to replicate the experiment, but you can replicate all the calculations with the raw data set, if put online. That's interesting.

Natural phenomena are decentralized. Anyone should be able to test whether your algorithm or statement about electrical fields is correct.

> Technological history is the history of what works; political history is the history of what works to retain power.

> Politics at its root is about tribes, not truth.

Politics masquerades as the search for truth, so people get taken in. But a truth that makes your tribe lose is a very unpopular truth. Truth is always beneficial in the long term. Copernican theory led to satellites. In the short term, though, you might have gotten burned at the stake.

Political truths—like money, status, and borders—are true if everyone believes them to be true. You can change these by rewriting facts in people's brains, such as: What is a dollar worth? Who is the president? Where is the border? These truths are what our establishment is set up to manipulate.

In politics, there's almost never an incentive to tell a truth that could annoy your tribe. A truth that leads to your tribe suffering a disadvantage is a truth that goes untold.

In politics, the normal incentives are reversed. Admitting an error costs personal status, while making an error only imposes costs on others. There are the people interested in your argument, and there are the people interested in distorting your argument.

Journalist Michael Kinsley says, "A gaffe is when a politician tells the truth—some obvious truth he isn't supposed to say."

> We select people who win popularity contests,
> then wonder why they're bad at allocating scarce
> resources.

This is the paradox of a free society. If it's really free, it may allow ideologies to flourish that want to stamp out society.

It's not just about free speech. It's about the cost of speech. If you're jailed by the state for speech, you may not speak out. But if you're fired by an employer for speech, that is costly too—a cost greater than most can pay. Costly speech means only the wealthy speak freely.

> The monopoly on truth is upstream of the monopoly
> on violence.

The opinions of others are imperfect proxies for analyzing the data yourself.

The more technical knowledge you have in an area, the less you need to rely on reputational signals. A few scientists publish a study; a few dozen people summarize it; a few million read the summaries. Then everyone argues with each other. Most of the nodes involved in that scenario are signal repeaters. What actually matters for determining truth are signal sources.

Signal repeaters are valuable because they bring items to your attention. Sometimes their summaries are even reliable. But the truth is upstream.

Data allows absolute reckoning of truth; reputation is relative reckoning. The internet makes it much easier to rely on data but much more common to rely on reputation.

People around you repeating the same idea may have gotten it from the same source. This fools our truth sensors, but **popularity does not equal truth.** There is no point debating someone who can't whip out plots, primary URLs, or raw data. Argue with signal sources, not signal repeaters.

Many people do not reason forward from logical premises, but backward from social consequences. This has its own logic because social capital is capital. Screaming at the outgroup is much cheaper than investing in the ingroup.

> Everybody has strong opinions about people they've never met based on tales told by people they do not know.

A great book called *The Gray Lady Winked* shows how we've been constantly gaslighted by the New York Times Company and other institutions. It's not just that the New York Times Company wrote itself out of causing the Iraq war with false information or wrote itself out of messing up the beginning of the COVID-19 pandemic with false information...it wrote itself out of other historical episodes too. The company has never actually had a good informational track record. It printed Nazi propaganda verbatim, Soviet propaganda verbatim, and Castro's propaganda verbatim. In many historical episodes, it was on the wrong side, and because it controlled the narrative later, it could rewrite history. You realize the extent of it when you go back in the archives and compare what its articles actually said to what it said they said. You realize, "Oh, that doesn't add up."

We have a huge problem in every area where social consensus determines truth. It's much, much deeper than people think.

Is it all a social construct?

Well, then, that means we can construct society.

ECONOMIC TRUTH

Popular opinion: platitude

Popular fact: triviality

Unpopular opinion: heresy

Unpopular fact: innovation

POPULAR

PLATITUDE	TRIVIALITY
HERESY	INNOVATION

OPINION

FACT

UNPOPULAR

Why do we need consensus on what can be measured? Why does this have to be decentralized? Having a base of undeniable truth to realign society around is super interesting. Here's why.

The first observation is: facts matter. Then the second-order observation is: facts *may not* matter, because if facts are just narratives told by competing tribes, then facts don't matter at all.

But the third-order observation is: facts *really do matter* because a narrative based on facts will, in the medium- to long-term, have more favorable contact with reality and therefore more technological and economic strength.

That last bit is critical. The reason the US eventually beat the Soviet Union is because communism required more lies. The Soviet Union had to make up factory production numbers because they didn't have prices, so supply chains didn't work, which meant factories didn't produce.

Holy lies, like the ones that animated the Soviet Regime, unfortunately work surprisingly well in the short term because you can bully or trick people into conforming with them. But in the medium- to long-term, they don't work. Your machines don't work, and your people don't work. You become poorer as a society. You're screaming these holy lies, but it doesn't matter because other societies who found real truths have exceeded you technologically and economically. That's why finding truths in a decentralized environment is important.

> More verifiable economic information enables more complex economic alignment.

Financial decision-makers will always care about truth. And crypto is turning the world into investors, just like the internet turned the world into publishers. Whether you have the scientific or historical evidence to prove a truth does not matter if people do not have an economic incentive for evaluating and then spreading that truth.

Even inside a company when gathering feedback for a company decision, collecting predictions rather than just doing a poll can be useful. Predictions can be aggregated like votes but also disaggregated for individual accountability. The individual accountability of a prediction is critical. It gives people an incentive to be correct even if unpopular. Most people evaluate whether something is really true or false only when they stand to win or lose money.

> Unpopular truth is a reliable source of profit. Behind every great fortune is a great thoughtcrime.

CRYPTOGRAPHIC TRUTH

Cryptocurrency has taken truths that were purely political and started to anchor them in technical truths.

Now we have an answer to what literal truth is through cryptography. Cryptography and how the blockchain manages information online provide decentralized truth—mathematical truths, which anybody has access to.

Everybody knows exactly how much Bitcoin you have, whether you're Palestinian or Israeli, Democrat or Republican. There's actually no contention over who owns what Bitcoin, which is amazing, because it's a trillion-dollar piece of international property. That's the kind of thing people usually fight over. That says something.

To have no dispute over who owns what Bitcoin is an absolute miracle of social technology. It's worth all of the energy and computing power required to mine it because people have conflicts for way less than a trillion dollars. Entire wars have been fought over much less. What Bitcoin achieved can now be generalized and applied to other areas. This is a huge innovation.

> The blockchain is the most important development in history since the advent of writing itself.

The blockchain contains a cryptographically verifiable, replicated, unfalsifiable, and provably complete digital record of a system. It's the ultimate triumph of the technological truth view of history because there are now technical and financial incentives for passing down true facts, regardless of the socio-political advantages anyone might have for suppressing them.

> You can't delete history anymore.

One particular piece of decentralized truth is most interesting to me: Crypto Oracles. Many of today's contracts or transactions are bets on things like, "Will this price go up or down?" or "Will the temperature go up?" A more complicated one: "Do I need to pay out this farmland insurance because there is a drought?"

That's an example of a contract that combines a financial function and a fact about the world. To execute automatically through a smart contract on the blockchain, the contract needs access to data about the outside world, which is not purely financial. That's what crypto oracles do.

Oracles broadcast data onto the blockchain, saying, "I, Weather Sensor 6, say it is 82 degrees in Poughkeepsie today, at this time." Then we get a timestamp of a temperature on-chain.

This will happen not just for temperature, but for crime statistics. It will happen not just for crime statistics, but for individual crimes from which statistics can be calculated. It will happen for medical records. A hospital won't have to actively count and report, "We have 1,000 coronavirus patients"; it will actually have a feed of "This patient at this time, that patient at that time." Redfin or Zillow won't publish just aggregate stats; they will provide a feed of real estate transactions happening in real time.

From all of these feeds of individual actions, aggregate stats can be computed, but you can also drill down to the individual rows in the data to do due diligence.

What's the point? Right now all of the data I'm describing are in separate places. The real estate data happens here, the medical data happens there, the price data happens way over there, the temperature data happens somewhere else. What I call the "ledger of record" is essentially the integration of all these crypto oracles.

People put data on-chain because they will earn money for supplying it. People pay for the information because they can trade off of it or use it to provide services. Each individual oracle has an incentive to put its data online. The data of all of those individual oracles go into the ledger of record, which gives us cryptographically verifiable facts about the world.

> Crypto oracles are more important than people think. Today it's global consensus on price history; tomorrow it's global consensus on history.

Essentially all human behavior has a digital component now. Every purchase, every communication, every Uber ride, every keycard swipe, and every step with a Fitbit—all produce digital artifacts. In theory, you could eventually download the public blockchain to replay the entire cryptographically verified history of a community. That's the future of public records. This is to our current paper-based system what paper records are to oral records.

We have digital documentation on an unprecedented scale. We have billions of people using social media each day for almost a decade now. Billions of phones taking daily photos and videos. Countless data feeds of instruments. Massive hard drives to store it all.

Measured in raw bytes, the information we now record in a single day is more than all of humanity had recorded up to the year 1900. Today, we have the most comprehensive log of human activity we've ever had.

Without cryptographic truth, there is only blind faith. Did Jesus rise from the dead? Well, someone must have hashed that video to the blockchain. Show us the timestamp and proof-of-work chain. It'll take a while, but eventually immutable timestamped recordings of almost every significant human event will be generated. Then, the highest truth comes not from faith in God or trust in the state, but from the ability to check the math of the network.

Assuming the concept of cryptocurrency can endure the invention of quantum decryption, future humans may think of the beginning of cryptographically verifiable history as being on par with the beginning of written history millennia ago. Future societies may think of the year 2022 AD as the year 13 AS, with "After Satoshi" as the new "Anno Domini" and the block clock as the new universal time.

You have a digital history, an unalterable history.
Everyone can know what happened when.

How to change the world:

1. Discover true facts.
2. Acquire sufficient distribution.

I said I was a pragmatic ideologue, and this is why. I'm an ideologue about discovering true facts and pragmatic about acquiring sufficient distribution.

It's unusual for someone to consciously combine discovering true facts and executing to acquire sufficient distribution, via money or followers. You need to learn how to make media clips and movies, write, publish, direct, encapsulate, build relationships, and build political coalitions; you need to learn how to fight.

I come into every discussion with the assumption that I need to justify everything from scratch. I take nothing for granted. I'm used to having people quibble with every word and every statement.

Non-obvious truths are always unpopular in some way, because they are either very technical or very sacrilegious. Popular communication channels are biased toward telling you obvious things or false things—or both.

I worry about how to protect the ability to discover true facts. We need a huge variety of reproducible research. The pseudonymous economy is important because to discover and share true facts, people need protection from backlash or cancellation.

For whatever comes next, we need to have decentralized sources of truth. We need to have statistics that do not come from guys in their basements making things up. This is very important.

We need to grow from "who owns what Bitcoin" today to "who said what things at what times" in the future. We will know what facts were asserted, when, and by whom. That is a very powerful thing. With cryptography, we can start to displace media corporations as the source of truth.

MODERN MEDIA IS MISALIGNED WITH TRUTH

Media is like a shimmery mirror. Reality is on the far side, what you read is on the near side, and the media is controlling the middle.

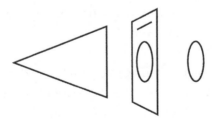

THEY CALL IT THE MEDIA BECAUSE IT MEDIATES
OUR INTERPRETATION OF REALITY.

YOU ARE WHAT YOU SEE

Code is how machines know what to do. Media is how humans know what to do. If you ran a computer program over your media diet, you could figure out what concepts you are reinforcing through repetition. The program could show "nutritional facts" on your media diet, like you see on your food.

A list of the top thousand keywords to pass through your screen would show you what you are loading into your brain. It might not necessarily be the concepts you want to learn.

> If you are what you eat, then you think what you see.

To restate the analogy between your nutritional and information diets: you are rebuilding your body with what you ingest with your mouth and rebuilding your brain with what you ingest with your eyes and ears. Put these two concepts together and you realize what you eat and what you read have enormous power over you.

Whether you agree or disagree with them, the information sources you choose will steer your life and establish your priorities. In a real sense, they are upstream of "you."

If you could somehow record everything you see and hear, you could determine advertising's actual effectiveness on you. How many times do you see an ad for Coke before you end up buying one?

We have physiological data that shows the effect of your diet on your metabolism. You can see your glucose spike after eating a cookie. Could we have graphs that show the effect of information diet on neurology? Could we see the dopamine spike after reading a tweet?

With wearable technology, we could detect changes in heart rate or blood pressure from viewing social media. Perhaps if we could see what it's doing to us, we might use it less.

It may be that humans get addicted to feeling righteous anger just like we get addicted to sugar, alcohol, or nicotine. If we can, social media is a superstimulus we need to identify and consciously limit in our information diets.

> If it enrages, it engages.

Emotionally aligning people against something appears easier than economically aligning people for something. Many writers and TV producers these days are like boxing promoters. They get two people to fight and make money from the spectacle.

Two people argue and fight over a stupid, intentionally polarizing idea. They might agree on 90 percent of other ideas. They might live in the same community, they might know each other from work or church, but they fight over a news article about a subject neither of them would have even thought to bring up—a topic the media optimized for being polarizing, creating these conflicts. The fighters both lose, but the publication makes money. It is negative sum at the system level.

A "scissor statement" is something that is obviously true to one party and obviously false to the other. Media and social media companies are constantly searching for and selecting scissor statements because they're enraging, and therefore engaging.

Media has an incentive to create conflict. Since legacy media corporations interrogate everybody else's incentives, it's worth asking what their incentives are. "If it bleeds, it leads." Well, that means there's an incentive to make it bleed.

Take war reporting—is it causing wars? Is it inflaming them?

Prolonging them? That happened with the Spanish American War. The yellow journalist William Randolph Hearst said, "You furnish the pictures, and I'll furnish the war."

We know there's at least one guy who basically started a war to sell papers, and we know war reporting juices profits; conflict juices profits. If the media makes more money in situations of conflict, they have a very bad incentive structure.

In 2013, the *New York Times* in particular started including a lot of "woke" keywords. With the right analytics, we can see they began juicing the "sugar content" of their articles by suddenly adding enraging words. At that time, the business was going badly. The *Washington Post* had just gotten bought by Bezos, legacy media was declining, and Google and Facebook were growing.

> Editorial judgment is more obvious in what is absent than what is present.

We hear so much about Zuckerberg, Kalanick, and Andreessen—all founders in tech—but most people cannot name the owners of media companies. It's not because owners of media companies get positive coverage; it's because they get no coverage.

We are being cautioned about Zuckerberg exerting editorial control over Facebook. We're not really focused on Sulzberger, who has indirect editorial control of the *New York Times* by appointing the editor-in-chief and the CEO.

Scrutiny is good. These media corporations should be scrutinized just as much as tech companies are for their editorial decisions, for their personnel, for their conflicts of interest, for their incentive structure.

The main things tech companies are attacked for, media companies also do. For example, a while back, an article by Kara Swisher in the *New York Times* attacked Zuckerberg for having dual-class shares. A few years before, an article by Joe Nocera celebrated the Sulzbergers for having dual-class shares. It's wildly inconsistent. Reporters will attack tech for having ad trackers while covering their own sites in ad trackers.

Individually, these arguments can work, but once you see them side by side, you're like, "Wait a second." This is not a universal argument; it's a tribal argument. It is arguing that media tribes should have power. That's really what it is. Media tribes should have power, and tech tribes should not. Media tribes can have dual-class stock; tech tribes cannot. These arguments have nothing to do with corporate governance. They have nothing to do with free speech.

This is how hierarchy is embedded. This is an implicit hierarchy, where someone can do something to you and you cannot do it to them, but it's not acknowledged explicitly. Once you look for this, you'll see it a lot. You "harass," but they "hold you accountable." You are "doxxing," but they are "investigating." These are the same actions described differently: "documents were obtained" versus "hacked documents were put on the internet illegally."

These are all linguistic tricks to embed a hierarchy in the conversation.

> Old: Trust one source to hear all sides.
>
> New: Hear all sides before trusting one source.

Here's a story: tech journalism is less diverse than tech. The technology industry is more diverse than the media outlets, who constantly challenge tech about their diversity. Oo Nwoye, executive director at TechCircle, tried to submit this story as an op-ed to a bunch of tech journalism outlets and couldn't get it published.

Another story: ownership of many of these media corporations is inherited. The owners are pure nepotists who received the family businesses from their fathers' fathers' fathers' fathers. Another aspect is they're mostly American, as opposed to the mostly immigrant nature of tech. Tech is very global and has a more international purview.

Narratives from media corporations conflict with their actions in many ways. Media corporations run billboards to market themselves as truth, democracy, and fairness. That is corporate propaganda, literally. It's propaganda from legacy media corporations to try to define themselves as truth. The brains of those working there have been melted by corporate propaganda to such an extent they really believe this.

Journalists, in general, are actually trusted about as little as politicians these days because they've been pushing themselves as the high priests of determining truth rather than showing their proof and process. Stories that favor their agendas are magnified 100x, while those that conflict are diminished 100x or silenced entirely. The net distortion of reality could be 10,000x or more.

> The story behind the story is usually more interesting than the story. Why this journalist? These sources? This tone? That omission?

Stephen Hawking tried to communicate nuance through the media. His point was completely lost because news is sold as entertainment. His interview was turned into hysterical headlines: "Stephen Hawking Is Terrified of AI," "Stephen Hawking Freaks Out," etc. (Here's a little-appreciated fact: many journalists lack control over their own headlines until they strike out on their own.)

Perhaps this is the first step in enlightenment: when someone asks, "Why don't you unconditionally trust media corporations?", you should ask how many articles they have personally independently replicated. Scientists know better than to blindly trust every paper.

THE *NYT* SAID ROCKETS COULD NEVER WORK

On January 13, 1920, the *New York Times* published an editorial insisting that a rocket couldn't possibly work in space.

The quote:

> That professor Goddard, with his "chair" in Clark College and the [financing] of the Smithsonian Institution, does not know the relation of action to reaction, and of the need to have something better than a vacuum against which to react—to say that would be absurd. Of course he only seems to lack the knowledge ladled out daily in high schools.

Goddard pushed back against a wave of criticism, unsuccessfully. He retreated from the public eye and from most interactions with other scientists but continued his research. Eventually, he'd be vindicated when a rocket launched in 1944 and the Apollo mission was completed in 1969.

It took until July 17, 1969, almost fifty years later, for the *New York Times* to take back its harsh words. The correction is almost comically dry and conspicuously doesn't mention the Apollo missions. "The *Times* regrets their error."

How much did this set back humanity? The Apollo missions might have happened decades earlier! Did you notice how they went after his grant funding? They said, "Why is the Smithsonian funding this guy?"

The journalist versus tech thing has been going on for so long. Matt Ridley writes about this in his book *How Innovation Works*. Ida Tarbell and a lot of other muckrakers went after Rockefeller and the other captains of industry who built America. They were all attacked by these journos in the early 1900s. Now we're fighting that same battle in reverse. I think this time the tech founders are going to win.

MEDIA HAS ITS OWN MOTIVES

1. Media companies are corporations.
2. Their interests are not always aligned with yours.
3. Act accordingly.

The one type of corporation a journalist will always defend is a media corporation. The one form of equality a journalist will always resist is the idea that everyone is now a journalist. A direct competitor is not a neutral arbiter.

Giving free content to media corporations in the form of quotes and interviews no longer makes sense. You must build your own distribution to avoid distortion. This is already happening. Elon, Zuckerberg, and all the smartest founders are building their own media arms, going direct and routing around legacy media corporations. Doing so is now a core competency. A CEO or a founder who does not build direct distribution is not doing it right. It's like a company not building a website.

The relationship between journalist and subject is hierarchical. There's a journalist (an employee of a media corporation) and the journalist's "subject." As in, "the subject under the microscope" or "a king and his subject" or "one who is subjected to." That word "subject" is such a revealing word. It gives away so much.

> Highly negative stories dominate headlines (if it bleeds, it leads), while highly positive outcomes determine returns (the power law).

Pageview-driven clickbait-headline media companies have put a lot of people out of business. They attack a lot of people. Their basic business model is to try to destroy somebody's reputation to earn $5 in clicks. That person's reputation is much more valuable to the person than $5.

Journos have perhaps even convinced themselves that publishing a disgruntled employee's story is a public service. But actually, doing so turns an internal personnel matter into a conflagration that reduces the company's stock price, making all employees poorer but gaining clicks for the media company who attacks. Journalists don't *actually* believe this is the proper way to handle personnel disputes because they sure aren't publishing their own disgruntled employee's takes!

With a clickbait business model, the goal is to maximally distort what somebody said so the headline is almost unbelievable, yet it has a very, very narrow connection to the truth. It's a massive distortion of what actually happened, but with enough truth that, in some interpretation, these media outlets can say it's not a flat-out lie. But they go to the absolute boundary of a flat-out lie.

They need readers to think, "Oh my God, that's unbelievable." Because what seems unbelievable gets retweeted. Media outlets have absolutely no incentive to tell the truth. They have incentive to play this game with the truth. They have incentive for getting clicks.

If you want to do one thing for your information diet on Twitter, do blocknyt.com. Block all establishment journalists. Right? It makes you less vulnerable to a crime of opportunity; you are out of sight, out of mind for them, and vice versa. You will see only peer-to-peer information, much less of their establishment's information. What we really want is entire boardrooms, entire companies, and entire countries who have totally blocked establishment journalists and shut them out.

One thing to keep in mind is that typically—but not always—people getting positive coverage in mainstream media are those that leak information to the press. They get rewarded later on with a profile or puff piece. It's not a monetary trade, but it's a trade worth dollars to both parties at some point.

If you realize the folks who get good coverage are the ones who leak, and the folks who are attacked are the ones who typically do not leak or cooperate with the press, then you realize reality may be an inversion of what you initially perceive.

> The term "story" indicates the importance of narrative in modern media. It's so easy to repeat a narrative.

The New York Times Company is worth $6.35B. It makes more than a billion dollars a year in revenue. It directly competes with tech for advertisers and influence. Not everything it publishes is "fake," but it's not a neutral arbiter. Neither are other media corporations. Everyone should act accordingly.

If you aren't running a corporation based on hereditary nepotism where the current guy running the show inherited the company from his father's father's father's father, you're more diverse and democratic than the owners of The New York Times Company. You don't need to take lectures from them, anyone they employ, or anyone under their social influence. You have the moral authority to hire who you need to hire, within the confines of the law.

HOW TO REALIGN MEDIA

The most constructive type of criticism is building an alternative. Yes, deconstruct the establishment. Use every verbal, technical, and monetary weapon we have. That is extremely important. But build something better. It is incumbent on us to build something better.

We need a different form of media all about relevance and skill building, an optimal information diet. What skills do you actually want to build?

> The media you consume changes the decisions you make.
>
> The technology you have changes the decisions you can make.

CREATING HIGH-VALUE MEDIA

Technology has recently been focused on software, but we should focus more on how media can increase people's skills and abilities. One path is creating media to help people create wealth. DIY YouTube videos are simple examples. The entire West Coast media ecosystem getting created now is implicitly focused on this. It's all about technology, building your business, and improving yourself.

> Maybe the new local news is by intellectual vertical, rather than geographic area.

This is not about monetizing a large mass of people. It is about serving people who really need to understand and comprehend an idea.

Imagine a site maintaining up-to-date information on 3D printing technology and all the companies in the industry, almost like an investment research report. A reader's goal may be to make an investment, join a company, or download a new program to start something or build something. This is a production-versus-consumption focus.

In reading this new type of media, you do not care about the headline, because reading the headline alone is not enough to do something. The real question is, what is the intent of people looking at this media? People who are consuming media just to be entertained do not have the incentive to actually understand something deeply.

The kind of media you want to consume when you consider your own performance is going to have a different business model than legacy media.

Journalist Gautham Nagesh said, "Content is a lousy business to be in, unless you've got information worth paying for." Put mathematically: differential profits from acting on an article must routinely exceed the differential cost of purchasing that information.

When you sell articles as entertainment, no action is expected. Articles to spur action are quite different. As a society, we've explored the depths of clickbait sites monetized by pageviews. But actionable information for different professions have not yet been fully explored.

> Twitter is a dispatch mechanism for our attention, in the same way Uber dispatches drivers to riders. You could imagine a very different dispatcher that maximizes long-term wealth creation.

Typically people will put war reporting and reporting on Kim Kardashian at opposite ends of the media spectrum: "This is super serious, Pulitzer-prize stuff" versus "This is fun infotainment." I argue they're actually both infotainment at the same end of the spectrum, and the other end is news-you-can-use and tutorials. The difference is whether a piece of information is directly relevant to your life. To identify at which end of the spectrum information belongs, consider:

are you going to spend the effort to confirm and *apply* every line of this information?

Coding tutorials have built-in fact checking because you have the tutorial on the left and your terminal on the right, and you're typing code line by line, verifying that it works. A You-Tube video showing you how to sew something or how to build a table works the same way. You're applying every line or every frame as you build.

Tutorials can't "lie" to you, not that they would want to. They can't misrepresent anything. They can't understate the complexity or overstate outcomes. Because they are instructional, you're learning and you're also fact checking as you use them, which is not obvious. People don't think about that part.

Other news-you-can-use is the weather or a stock price. This information determines an action. If it's rainy, I grab an umbrella. If the stock price is high, maybe I sell. If the stock price is low, maybe I buy. This information guides decisions. It's right next to tutorials on our new spectrum of media utility.

On the other end of the spectrum is reading about some issue in a distant country. Unless I have relatives, businesses, or operations there, it's not relevant to me on a daily basis. People might say, "You should be concerned about these things." The problem is there are seven billion people on the planet.

As a kind of toy experiment, think about this. There are 86,400 seconds in a day. In 12 days, if you learn one of those seven billion people's names per second, you could learn the names of a million people. It would take you 120 days for 10 million people; 1,200 days for a hundred million people; and 12,000 days for a billion people. Basically, it would take your whole life to even learn the names of the seven billion people on the planet. You cannot possibly care about them all equally. You have to triage or somehow prioritize. You have to rank-order what you're paying attention to.

Infotainment should be filtered out of your information diet. Returning to the analogy between your nutritional diet and your information diet...having a cookie from time to time is fine, but if you're eating only cookies and you're not eating healthy food, your health is going to be messed up. Your life is going to get worse.

I'm not saying never have fun. But Twitter and other social media are like restaurants that have learned to secretly put sugar in their food. Social media and streaming services are optimized to consume as many minutes of your day as possible. They are literally addictive.

MEDIA DRIVEN BY THE READER'S BENEFIT

If you look at Reddit, Twitter, Facebook, or similar platforms, you'll see something they have in common you won't be able to unsee: *randomness*. Literally, thirty random links. These platforms are optimized for novelty, like a slot machine.

Every day, first thing, most people get a blend of randomness all at once. In this high-dimensional space, you're being pulled in a bunch of different directions, not really making progress. Progress is doing some math today and doing some more math in the same area tomorrow. A little bit of compounding progress along the same direction each day adds up to something, but time spent on these sites add up to nothing.

I'm not saying they have zero value; there's some value to serendipity. You do learn the pulse of what a community is thinking. But I think we are overconsuming novelty and underconsuming purpose.

What's the good stuff? It is what helps you boost the measurable variables you care about. It's increasing your truth, health, and wealth. It's your knowledge, your physical fitness, your bank account balance, or some combination of them.

Those are things you'd put on a personal dashboard. You should be trying to level up each day for you and your family. Then you're really making progress on these critical life variables.

Dashboards are better than newspapers. If you are in tech, the first thing you look at each work day may be a company dashboard with metrics, like sales. This is good. The first thing you look at personally each day shouldn't be random stories someone else picked. It should be carefully selected metrics you want to improve, like your health or hobbies. A personal dashboard is a good path to disrupt newspapers.

> Algorithms and incentives **could** surface what is important and true rather than what is popular and profitable.

What if media was designed to be driven by the reader's benefit? What could *Men's Health* look like in the era of Fitbit? What would *Bloomberg* look like if it measured whether its content improves your portfolio over time? What if educational publishers measured whether you actually retain information over time?

> This type of media has a totally opposite design goal, which is to give maximum value in a minimum amount of time.

Building the next *Men's Health* when all your readers have Fitbits, Apple Watches, or smart scales means you can see the cause and effect of your content. You don't just write, "Here are great abs!" You write, "Here are step-by-step instructions on how to improve your diet," and you actually see the change in weight of your readers.

You start tracking something completely differently, which is to the reader's benefit. This is a new concept for basically all health magazines. All fitness content could immediately do this. Enough health tracking devices are out there now.

We need better metrics. You want a stream of data coming out of you. You want alerts on your blood sugar, O2 capacity—all that kind of stuff. Those are the most important metrics, right?

That is news you can use, news where the locus of control is you; you can do something about it. Imagine your personal dashboard for your own fitness, diet, and sleep, and then maybe a family dashboard.

This type of dashboard would be more useful to you than Twitter or Facebook. It would be the right app to check each day. Then, informed by your dashboard, you could take other actions. Other media you would treat as junk food.

Everything I'm describing already exists. But integrating these technologies and making the habit to check them the first thing every day is really important.

ALIGNING INCENTIVES FOR WRITERS

We need mechanisms to realign tech, media, and society. One concept is if your article or film inspires someone to found a great company that solves a social problem (e.g., fusion energy to address climate change), as the media creator, you get a share in cash or equity.

Inspiring journalists, filmmakers, and authors could be integrated into the financing pipeline to receive their fair shares. Some examples: Nicholas Kristof's article inspiring Bill Gates to create hygienic rural toilets in Africa, the *Minority Report* movie sparking Microsoft's Xbox Kinect, and the *Ready Player One* book inspiring Oculus.

If you, as a writer, add value to your reader, you could earn a fraction of that value. Many startups have been inspired by a piece of writing. Imagine if writers were to receive some equity in the companies they help start. This would change the writer's incentive structure from quantity to quality. Now, it doesn't matter how many pageviews you get. You're trying to find, say, the next Zuckerbergs or Vitaliks of fusion energy, attract them to your blog, and help them build.

You may have only 10,000 readers in the world. These may be the only people who care enough about nuclear fusion energy to consider it "news you can use." But some people using your work could create extremely valuable companies.

> The nepotists of New York versus the founders of the world?
>
> I know who I bet on.

Another piece of the solution could be to directly incentivize correctness. Imagine a new media outlet where every post is accompanied by a prediction market bet, and thus writers have personal skin in the game. This kind of news would be by investors, for investors. You might not even use the term reporter.

The closest we have today are VC blog posts on investments and crypto journalists with disclosed crypto holdings. A prediction-betting feature would align reader/writer incentives.

Prediction markets may not actually predict the future, but they do keep pundits accountable and put them on the record. Starting a media company where all writers are hired on the basis of their prediction track records would be interesting. Making public bets in prediction markets puts pundits on record in a timestamped, quantifiable, unfalsifiable way. (A number of the smarter journalists are becoming venture capitalists, which is a related trend.)

I want a tool to parse tech journalists' predictions and convert them into a public record of picks. We could backfill previous years from their existing writing. The resulting rank ordering would let you know who correctly called the future. Then we could uprank the authors with early positive sentiment toward winners, especially if writers' predictions were early and contrarian.

And then we could expose all that data in an application programming interface (API), which we could use as a novel input to media outlets. Journalists with good long-term prediction accuracy would earn more traffic and better reputations. It would be like star ratings for authors/bloggers/tweeters, which is probably also useful for Google. It would totally counter the snarky clickbait-for-traffic trend. You skip YouTube videos with clickbait titles and 1-star ratings, but we don't have that for news articles. Ratings of articles is an obvious missing component in media.

BUILDING A FACT-BASED MEDIA

Technology isn't really covered that well today. Western media covers only funding rounds. Why? Because they can't explain the math or science. They can't assess it from that angle. So they reduce the story to money and personalities.

You can learn a lot from expert commentary. Articles on tech in particular could benefit from pre- or at least post-publication peer review by experts in the field (investors, engineers, and founders).

We could create a system to go line-by-line on every tech article to independently check facts. We could do this in a semi-decentralized way. For an article with 100 sentences, at $10/sentence, that's about $1k. At four tech articles per day, 365 days per year, that's "only" about $1M/year.

Backlinks and search engines are powerful tools for checking sources manually, but automatically digesting text to find sources with URLs is the next level. For example, we could autodigest news articles to find the source press releases or papers.

HOW MEDIA GETS US TO MARS

"Do you want to get to Mars or just write articles about it?" Well, it turns out we are going to have to write articles about Mars—lots of them—to get to Mars. For any technology we want to drive forward, we must own the discourse.

Bitcoin taught us this. If you write with more energy and more zeal than opponents, technology will win in the long run. And we don't need just writing. We need art, literature, and movies too.

> You don't have to be a rocket scientist to post supporting them.

Imagine an NBA game where players believe they're playing for the same team, but only see their own points. That's how ideological movements work on social media today; we see only individual profiles, no team dashboards.

Here is how we can take a data-driven approach: Find a technology you want to advance. Analyze the sentiment around it. Determine how much content you'd have to create to swing sentiment. Then swing it.

Legacy media corporations try to optimize for prestige but often settle for optimizing for clicks. They need to pay the bills. Clicks and prestige are both measurable (the latter by awards), but both are legacy measures.

On the other hand, optimizing for *sentiment* around a keyword like "Mars" or "Bitcoin" is something new. It's essentially pure activism. An organization optimizing for creating sentiment around Mars or life extension would get very different results. Sentiment was hard to measure until recently, thanks to Natural Language Processing (NLP), a computer's ability to understand human language.

Prioritizing changing sentiment instead of clicks means creators stay ethical and avoid the trap of creating clickbait. We can all found, fund, and patronize personal media corps committed to key ideas, such as faster drug testing, self-driving cars to cut traffic fatalities, or nuclear fusion to stop climate change.

Any thesis for positive change through technology can be turned into a media company. We can fund creators to produce amazing content on life extension, brain-machine interfaces, or colonizing Mars.

Clicks and prestige would be zero-sum metrics for a decentralized activist community, but sentiment is not. You're convincing the external world something is a good idea. Fill up the sentiment bar, and we can go to Mars.

BUILDING A BETTER TRUTH MACHINE

SOCIAL MEDIA IS A HUGE VAT OF BRAINS

People are running on scripts. They don't even realize they're running on scripts. Media scripts humans, just as computer code scripts machines.

When kids come out of a movie theater, they immediately start quoting lines and re-enacting what they just saw on the screen. Sometimes you can get people to do something by telling them to do it, but often just showing it being done is better.

Humans are mimetic. We mimic each other to acquire language and align on objectives. You could call it "contagious mental states." I think this is an understudied concept. We know there are contagious physical illnesses, like viruses. Now consider contagious mental illnesses.

We all stuck our brains into Twitter. Being on Twitter is like putting your brain into a vat with 300 million other peoples' brains who are all sending their brain-states to you electromagnetically. It feels a little unhygienic if you think about it that way. We create social distance offline, but we pack closely together online. Bad memes and crazy ideas spread faster than ever, because all our brains are connected.

If you go to Google Trends and type in a recent headline, you'll see the topic often goes totally vertical. Everybody cares about the topic suddenly. Then interest in the topic drops off just as quickly. People go manic over something they didn't even know about two weeks ago. It's life and death to them; they're willing to fight, kill, and burn things down. Then, three weeks later, they don't care at all and will never care again.

The offline world doesn't reward rudeness to random strangers. Twitter, unfortunately, does. From an incentives standpoint, I think that is the problem. Starting fights on Twitter attracts followers. Followers are valuable. Starting fights in the physical world attracts police attention. That is not valuable. Ethics restrains many people—but not everyone, and not always.

My overall intuition is we need a totally new incentive-based approach to social networking now that we see failure modes at scale. Building Google was hard until seeing several years of Yahoo.

> Popularity can be measured by likes. Truth can't be.
>
> Status is a zero-sum game. Wealth creation isn't.

Lots of popular ideas on social media are a result of consistent repetition rather than independent replication. In cryptocurrency, we use the concept of independent confirmations. You don't approve a transaction right away. You wait for six independent confirmations.

Our mechanisms for information dissemination have advanced past our mechanisms for information verification. Fortunately, the information is electronic, on a screen, in a database. Maybe soon some of the truth can catch up to the lies.

> Everyone thinks the censor will agree with them.
>
> Actually, the censor will censor them.

Important new communication technologies often tear down trust in an existing system. They allow distribution of truths the old system was censoring.

This is another reason technology is a driving force in history. All ideologies have existed for a long time. Read Plato and you will see some of the same political ideas. What changes is communication technology.

The time selects for the technology, and the technology selects for the ideology.

The era of centralized technology had mass production and mass media. The political ideologies enabled by those technologies were Communism, Nazism, and Democratic Capitalism. For the past hundred years, they slugged it out.

In this new decentralized era, those ideologies are not benefited by current technologies. Instead, new ideologies grow through networks, like wokeness or cryptocurrency. These ideologies are transmitted on social media, the opposite of a top-down authoritarian-enabling technology.

> If an idea requires censorship to maintain its continued popularity, it may not be a good idea.

The Spanish flu was censored. The Katyn Forest, where the USSR killed a bunch of Poles and Polish leaders and lied about it, was covered up. These truths could have broken trust in the regime if they were public, but they were kept secret.

With the printing press, Martin Luther delegitimized the Catholic Church by calling out things like indulgences (sin forgiveness in exchange for payment). Many people probably had an issue with the practice in private. But when Martin Luther printed and shared his critiques, a new public consensus formed outside the control of the existing regime. That started the Reformation.

With crypto, we have something similar to the printing press.

THE FUTURE OF MEDIA IS DECENTRALIZED

We are moving from mainstream media through social media to our destination: decentralized media; that is, decentralized reporting, sourcing, hosting, distribution, payments, bounties, predictions, reputation, verification, consensus, and truth.

We need a better truth machine. The answer is not a new media company. It's a new media community with fundamentally different premises: global, not East Coast; one hundred people part-time, not one person full-time; scientific depth over narrative. This kind of media would be representative of the people, because it is the people.

> The supplicant bemoans the problems of centralization.
>
> The technologist builds the decentralized solution.

A shared issue for legacy media and social media is that their content is not open source. Since the content is proprietary, restricted by copyright and API access, the public can't create its own arbitrary views of the data. What's the alternative? Decentralized media.

An excellent example is the GitHub repository with records of police brutality behind 2020pb.com. Because it is fully open source, anyone can submit a pull request (contribution), it's free to access, all the primary sources are verifiable, pseudonymous submission is okay, there is a full revision history, and the data is forkable (copyable) and downloadable.

As the Fourth Estate, the press sees its role as holding others in society accountable. As the Fifth Estate, social media is how society holds the press accountable. You can't have an "informed citizenry" if citizens can't inform other citizens. The concept of social media as the Fifth Estate may be the most enduring part of Mark Zuckerberg's contribution.

> The right to voice is as important as the right to vote.

CREATING PRE-NARRATIVE NEWS

What could the 10x better version of the *New York Times* look like?

→ Revision control for all articles
→ Open source NLP tools
→ Reproducible journalism with citations
→ Citizen journalists rather than corporate journalists
→ Decentralized fact checking

Maybe this is the "raw" news feed journalists and investors themselves read? This is what Reuters purported to be, a neutral feed. It is pre-narrative news. Sports scores or a stream of stock price movements are closer to this today.

This is a key observation: **many pieces of media are words or video wrapped around public data structures.** Sports articles are often wrappers around box scores. Financial articles are often wrappers around a company's financials. Many articles and news broadcasts are wrappers around tweets.

News eventually will all be based on event feeds. Today many events are digitally logged to separate databases. Eventually, this will become one giant feed. Private data will be encrypted, and public entries will be linkable. This kind of global on-chain event feed would take over from newspapers as the true first draft of history.

Digital timestamps can be used to establish everything from the reality of a patent to the fakeness of a photo. Citizen journalists can take these emotion-stripped "raw" facts and then add their own narratives on top to make sense of them.

Another interesting idea is to downrank polarizing content. Content analysis to find and measure polarizing words and scissor statements can be done in real-time today. It's much easier than fact checking.

Facebook or Twitter could do this today if they wanted to. So could the *New York Times* and *Wall Street Journal*. But doing so would hurt engagement, and therefore profit.

An "important feed" will be very different from the "news feed." What is important often is not new, and what is new often is not important.

SEPARATING FACTS FROM NARRATIVES

My vision of the future of media involves oracles and advocates. An oracle might be a sensor writing data on-chain. It could be a machine that takes the temperature. You might think that's trivial, but having lots of them would be valuable. You could use a cryptographically provable record in discussions about climate, for example.

Oracles are the first layer, the base layer. They provide raw facts—information directly from sensors. A sensor could lie to you; it could say the temperature is 80 when it's actually 30, but the sensor has a digital signature, so you can see its track record, compare it to other sensors, audit, filter/correct, and let other people audit too.

Advocates are the second layer, on top of oracles. Advocates are humans. We assume humans have editorial judgment. They choose not just what to write, but what to write about.

The selection of specific facts advocates choose to include in an article is itself visible. Editorial judgment is now quantifiable because you have a layer of raw facts on-chain behind the article. The narrative becomes tangible because it shows **which** facts writers cite in their stories. Fact selection is now quantifiable; we can see not just what was included but, crucially, what was omitted.

Oracles and advocates are two key ideas in decentralized media—factoring things into either pure facts (oracles) or pure narratives (advocates).

Each media outlet could have a version-controlled public list of keywords for which they are clear, unapologetic advocates.

Subscribers and donors could fund the outlet on the basis of their fidelity to the cause. This is using technology for values alignment.

The ledger of record is the combination of all feeds of on-chain data. It subsumes social media feeds, data APIs, event streams, newsletters, and RSS. It'll take years to build but will ultimately become the decentralized layer of facts that underpins all narratives.

Think of the ledger of record as a decentralized wire service. Every person and organization slowly moves from posting on centralized social media platforms to posting on decentralized protocols. Decentralized media will have monetization, permissions, distribution, and programmability built in.

> "News" isn't an article; it's a graph. A graph of posts, images, and videos from many parties.

> Own a media corporation or be owned by one.

If writing the Great American Novel on your laptop or building a billion-dollar startup in your dorm room is possible, breaking the story of the year as a citizen without any access to traditional institutions is absolutely possible.

I believe in citizen journalists for the same reason I believe in solo developers. Satoshi showed what one person can do. So did Snowden. In 2013, Snowden needed the help of the courageous Glenn Greenwald, but the next Snowden could do the whole thing independently.

Writing is fighting. It's not obvious, but no one is covering many tenured bureaucrats with god-level powers. A citizen journalist with expertise in a government-blocked area can reform obsolete regulations by cultivating sources, writing articles, and naming names.

Just like the open-source culture transformed closed-source software corporations into something more ethical, more open, *and* more commercially viable, decentralized media would strive to do the same.

> We have fiduciary responsibility to our shareholders.
>
> Is there infoduciary responsibility to our subscribers?

The founding fathers' concern over a standing military was that it was separate from the people. It was a class with special powers and therefore temptation. A standing media is similar. The solution to both is citizen involvement. If you don't do journalism, someone will do it to you.

The answer is NOT to found a new typical media company. After all, new media companies like Vice, Vox, and BuzzFeed all found themselves pulled into the same culturally centralized Brooklyn media circle. Different companies, same people, same social network.

This is why we need to decentralize media. Twitter was version one of decentralized media, and Substack is version two. We're moving toward individual citizen journalists and away from media corporations. Perhaps we will see "full stack writers" who go from writing articles to producing movies themselves, like the full stack developer.

Some principles:

1. Every citizen is a citizen journalist.
2. Every company is a media company.
3. Media scales.

Great journalists might become millionaires, or even billionaires. Don't option the movies; make them yourself on your computer like Notch made Minecraft, and then sell it directly. Nate Silver and Andrew Sorkin are early versions of this type of journalist. There may be room for a Y Combinator of personal media corporations.

JOINING A NEW MEDIA COMMUNITY

"Dollowers" (dollar-weighted followers) are an important part of the future. Normal followers are nonpaying commenters, and subscribers are quiet paying supporters. But dollowers are engaged *and* pay creators. They often support individuals rather than institutions.

Platforms like Substack, Patreon, and Ghost allow writers to optimize for dollowers. Dollowing is a scarce and valuable behavior, unlike following. In the battle of ideas, dollowing is more important than following or just retweeting. We could compile lists of people who deserve support and organize mass financial support of those creators.

Unlike local newspapers, new media communities gather for an ideology instead of geography. Individual writers are accountable for their own work. Then the new "newspapers" are dynamic bundles of different individual's work.

Crypto payments protect everyone's privacy, prove who is actually a supporter, and allow support across borders. Eventually, crypto will allow creators to cite on-chain events as a way of proving predictions or preventing deletion. A community of 10,000 folks spending $1,000 per year could support one hundred individual creators at $100k/year. Virtue signaling could become value signaling. For example: How much have you done to support creators in our community? And what have you created?

Now, $1,000/year is not trivial; some might be able to contribute only $100 or even $10. But $1,000 is within reach of many people, especially if they truly believe in a cause. Financially supporting a cause gives people who want to do something a concrete *something* to do. Either fund or create, either dollow or build. This applies to open source software, art, writing, and more. We can have a community of engineers, artists, and writers all working toward a common goal, supported by dollowers.

> Good writers and artists should be rewarded. We just need to change the incentives.

People who know math and science, who have experience in managing and investing, who are *technological progressives* rather than technological conservatives—these people need to learn to write, report, publish, and direct. We need to consciously build a parallel tech-driven decentralized media ecosystem, and we need it to become the first port of call for anyone seeking to learn about technology.

In this we will have allies around the world. Only the very richest people can afford to be cynical about the merits of technological progress. The billions of people who just got their first smartphones had their lives dramatically improved. They are too pragmatic to romanticize the past.

People with scientific and technical backgrounds have not taken it upon themselves to write about technological progress as a duty. We need to take time out of our busy days to make the case, repeatedly and with high production values, that technological progress is the most important thing we can do for broad prosperity, economic growth, and for life itself.

We may not get life extension or the whole suite of transhumanist technologies (brain-machine interfaces, stem cells, CRISPR gene therapy, and more) unless you, personally, evangelize them online. Not just with tweets, but with articles. Not just with articles, but with videos. Not just with videos, but with feature films. Not with just a few films, but with an entire Netflix original library's worth.

We need to create a parallel media ecosystem full of inspirational content for technological progressives—a lifetime's worth of content that makes the case for immutable money, infinite frontier, and eternal life.

Media corporations are against free speech for the same reason Microsoft was against free software. They are for-profit corporations that want to eliminate all competitors.

But they'll lose. Every citizen is becoming a journalist, and every company is becoming a media company.

PART III

BUILDING
THE FUTURE

To get lucky, you must first take a chance.

BELIEVING

ADOPT A MINDSET OF ABUNDANCE

> As a guiding philosophy, "win and help win" will always outcompete "live and let live."

You want a win-win mentality rather than a crabs-in-the-bucket mentality. A win-and-help-win mentality is even better. Your win helps you help me win, and vice versa. Win and help win is actually the profit maximizing strategy in the long term. When crabs-in-a-bucket don't have enough resources, nobody ends up with resources because everybody is getting pinched. Win and help win is actually how technology and venture capital works.

We have bad metrics as a society. Rather than GDP, GDP-per-capita, or the stock market, perhaps we should have dashboards of life expectancy (health) and net worth (wealth). A good leader is one who improves these metrics for individuals and society as a whole.

Here is my reasoning: most people can't tell you how to compute GDP, but they can tell you what net worth and life expectancy are. They know what it means for those numbers to go up, and they know making them go up is valuable. If these numbers have gone up for you, your life has improved.

Good: Helping others without concern for yourself

Smart: Helping others while helping yourself

Evil: Harming others while helping yourself

Stupid: Harming others while harming yourself

On the internet, we see more upsides and more downsides in everything. Technologists focus on the upside, because the gains should compound, while the losses should be individual events. Once you find a winning formula, you can scale it quickly to make it cheap. This leads to even *more* net upsides over time, just like every past technological revolution has.

Without something to build, any intellectual movement degenerates into a status competition, where participants feel the righteousness of finding everyone else wanting without the responsibility of building what they actually want.

CREATING YOUR OWN WEALTH

Many people don't understand that wealth can be created. My first counterexample for them: who did Steve Jobs steal all the iPhones from? If wealth is a zero-sum game, where one person's gain is someone else's loss, where did the phones come from? This simple example shows wealth can be created. A surprising number of people seem to believe profit is a function of sufficient malevolence. Wealth creation always attracts entitled predators.

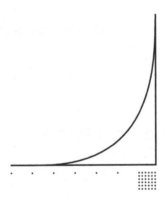

EVERYONE WANTS A PIECE OF THE REWARD,
NO ONE WANTS A PIECE OF THE RISK.

The fewer people you employ in the process of wealth creation, the harder it becomes for people to claim that you "exploited" others. Some software entrepreneurs make billions by themselves, like J.K. Rowling did writing books. Satoshi Nakamoto (Bitcoin) and Notch (Minecraft) are early examples.

The closer value creation comes to pure authorship—symbols typed straight from the mind—the harder it is to deny the merit of the person who generated those symbols.

You can write a piece of software on a computer and then set up a website, and people will pay money for your software. What are you actually doing there? With no natural resources, just by hitting keys, you created a pleasing configuration of electrons.

At a very fundamental level, you created order from disorder. You created a more useful configuration of zeroes and ones from random order. The internet allows you to clone and export your creation to millions of users around the world who just click to pay for it.

> Power compels; money persuades.

We don't have the right metrics to measure wealth creation yet. We can measure the profit and loss of a business, but we don't yet have a widely accepted way of quantifying the wealth produced by voluntary transactions with a business.

Money seems to be locally zero-sum (after a trade happens, Person A has –$1, Person B has +$1), but actually money is globally positive-sum. In a voluntary exchange, A and B both gain in wealth because they both get non-monetary benefit from making the trade.

Wealth creation is the technological creation of order. It is the difference between a bunch of bricks lying on the ground and a house; the difference between a bunch of pieces of wood lying on the ground and a chair. You can see those differences in physical space.

When people are confused about wealth creation in a physical example, they say, "You must have gotten the bricks from somebody. You must have gotten the wood from somebody." Most of the value, though, is in the ordering of those materials. Often the value of raw materials is not anywhere near the value of the assembly process: the know-how, the machines, and the effort required to put the raw materials together.

The examples on a computer (like a new piece of software) are more obvious because they are pure—the materials have no cost. The new creation is just an electron configuration. Nobody says you took that from somebody else.

> The less money you need, the less dependent you are.

When you're in any institution, you cannot speak freely, especially when you're the CEO. I've only really been able to speak freely to a greater extent over the last year and a half.

After my first big liquidity event, I had around ten years of personal runway (the number of years one can go without working). That's when I became kind of invincible, in a sense. Saving money and separating from organizations made me intellectually independent. It was like giving myself tenure.

I don't buy cars or homes. After I earned a big payout, whenever I could save time with money, I did. That's the single biggest change I have made. I spend my money on being able to work harder. It sounds funny, but it's true.

I'm not a consumption person; I'm a production person. I'm not burning capital on stuff. Everything is going into the next compounding outcome—not just compounding money, though money is an important tool. Knowledge compounds on other knowledge. Impact, same thing.

> Once you get that first win under your belt, you build the confidence you're able to do it again and again.

Reducing your cost of living to ⅕x is way easier than increasing your net worth by 5x. If you're willing, you can move to the middle of nowhere and cut your expenditures. You can just read Kindle and live on simple, healthy foods. You can basically reduce your consumption to the level of a grad student.

Then you can go from making, say, 120k in San Francisco and spending 100k a year and having no savings to making 120k in Bali, Indonesia, but only spending 30k or 40k a year with a better quality of life. Now you're banking 70k or 80k a year, and your expenditures are only 40k a year. So every single year you work, you're building up one or two years of time off. That's time off you can use to start a company. It's like angel investing in yourself. This is another way you can become financially independent.

Build your personal runway. Here is the basic calculation for reducing your expenses to become financially independent:

$$[\text{your current savings}] \div [\text{your yearly expenses}] = [\text{personal runway}]$$

Financial independence is also personal and ideological independence. If you have financial independence, the crowd can't economically cancel you. If you have a financial cushion, which anybody can build by cutting consumption, you can ride out challenges.

**THE ULTIMATE MORNING ROUTINE IS TO BE ABLE
TO WAKE UP WHENEVER YOU WANT.**

STARTING SMALL

Today, we associate startups with Silicon Valley, computer science, and venture capital. In the past, it was other businesses, like oil, steel, pharmaceuticals, and telegraphs in the 1800s of the US. The automobile, aviation, and telephone industries can all be characterized as "past startups."

Eli Lilly and Company is a huge pharmaceutical conglomerate that started out of the back of a pharmacy. Colonel Eli Lilly created a medical wholesale company while working in the back of a drugstore. His first year of business sales were $4,470. Seeing how these companies started out is pretty interesting. When you think about oil, steel, or pharmaceuticals, you do not think, *I'm gonna go and start that in a garage*. But that's what these people did.

Samuel Kier started an oil refinery on Seventh and Grant in downtown San Francisco, which is insane. An oil refinery is a multibillion-dollar facility. To visualize starting one in your apartment in a city is almost laughable; it's astonishing to think that's where the oil refining industry began.

In 1921, Banting and Best came up with the idea of using insulin to treat diabetes. By 1922, they had extracted insulin, tested it on themselves, tested it on animals, and put it in a patient's arm. In 1923, Banting and Best won the Nobel Prize.

A timeframe like this is now impossible given the constraints of today's regulatory environment. Shipping a drug takes ten years and four billion dollars. This is a very important point: you can't just ship a drug. You can't have a drug company whose philosophy is to move fast and break things, at least not in the modern United States. You would need a much more risk-tolerant environment, and that's not where we are today.

When aviation was invented, there was no Boeing and no FAA. From 1903 until the Air Commerce Act of 1926, the skies were wide open, without many rules. Fatal crashes were a common occurrence...and two Wright Brothers could start an airplane company out of a bike store.

> Can you believe the Wright brothers went into the air without approval from the FAA or *any* kind of collective decision-making?
>
> They decided to fly just because they could.

These pioneers had some time before competitors and regulations created barriers to entry. The messy process of innovation resulted in many deaths from refinery fires, railroad collisions, car explosions, airplane crashes, and drug overdoses. At first, this was accepted as the price of progress.

Over time, competitors with higher-quality products arose, and regulations effectively criminalized the sale of beta-quality products. Barriers to entry rose, increasing the capital required to challenge incumbents. In these industries, starting a company in your garage became much more difficult.

The most important features of those industries early on were: (1) Low cost of capital to start a business, and (2) Wide-open regulatory, technological, and physical frontiers.

FINDING A FRONTIER

Without a frontier, it all becomes zero-sum.

When fighting over any scarce resource, if one group teams up and the other doesn't, the first group tends to win. This is the fundamental reason humans tend to consolidate into two factions and fight each other over scarce resources until one faction wins. The winning team enjoys a brief honeymoon, after which it often divides into new left and right factions, and the battle begins again.

After the French Revolution, factions arose. After World War II, the once-allied US and USSR began the Cold War. After the Cold War, the victorious US broke into internal hyperpolarization. A strong leader might keep this from happening for a while, but the division of a victorious group into left and right factions is almost a law of societal physics.

Everything changes when a frontier opens up. A new realm of unoccupied space means resources are suddenly less scarce. An aggrieved group can choose flight rather than fight. The would-be revolutionary doesn't have to try to overthrow the ruling class anymore. Those who don't like the current order can leave for the frontier.

In the late 1800s, American historian Fredrick Jackson Turner gave an influential talk about the frontier as the driving force in American history. He said the frontier was crucial to the US in several ways: as a path for the ambitious to seek their fortunes, as a national aspiration (Manifest Destiny), and with bare land as a canvas for social experiments.

Closing the frontier took paths away from ambitious people

because they couldn't easily become founders on their own plots of land. They became union organizers, revolutionaries, or demagogues. Without the frontier, it all became zero-sum.

This pattern has occurred throughout history. Europe and North America had a period of greatness during an open frontier from 1492–1890 and a period of total war during the closing frontier from 1890–1991.

Technology is how civilizations unlock new frontiers. Columbus used new navigation techniques to find the new world because the Ottomans had blockaded the known route to India. The internet has actually been the frontier for the past few decades, and with crypto, that will likely continue.

> People forget how completely non-obvious the entire digital revolution has been every step of the way.
>
> 1995: "WWW will fail."
>
> 2002: "Google will fail."
>
> 2007: "iPhone will fail."
>
> 2013: "Facebook will fail."

The peaceful reopening of the digital frontier could lead us again to a time of greatness. The American and Chinese establishments are trying to close that frontier. That would trap us into the same steel cage match we experienced in the 20th century.

With sufficient technology and wisdom, we can escape these political roadblocks. We can reopen not just a digital frontier, but a physical one: on remote pieces of land, on the sea, and eventually in space.

Today, there are four possibilities for the frontier: the land, the internet, the sea, and space. If we assess where we are right now, we learn that currently 7.7B people are on land, 3.2B on the internet, about 2–3M on the high seas, and fewer than 10 in space.

Creating frontiers is important. Frontiers give pioneers space to innovate without affecting those who don't consent to the experiment.

BAD LEADERS DIVIDE. GREAT LEADERS CREATE.

> Nothing is more costly than incompetent leadership.

Here is my ranking of types of leaders: socialist < nationalist < capitalist < technologist.

Why does socialism keep arising over and over again? One way of answering that question: it is the easiest way to become a leader.

In any functional society, you can just start yelling that 51 percent is oppressed by 49 percent. That will always work to get attention and arouse passion. You can find some unjust axis and start agitating that issue. Conflict gets attention, and attention is currency. If you're shameless, you level up. Socialism is the lowest-skill way to put yourself at the head of a mob. This and variants on it, like demagoguery, will work in almost every country. You're pitting some faction against another.

One step up from socialism, we have nationalism: unifying one nation against the other side of the border. The good part about nationalism is it stops the conflict internally. People are aligned internally because of a common cause. That's the good part. The bad part about nationalism is that often people are so enthusiastic that they move from nationalism (or patriotism) into much worse jingoism, chauvinism, or imperialism.

One level up from nationalism, we have capitalism. Now we're unifying people on the basis of a common cause in the market. Now defeating the other guys doesn't mean killing them or starting a war; it means fighting them in the market in a voluntary way where they can submit peacefully. You're virtualizing the conflict. Capitalism is positive-sum because you're creating something of value. You can lead a very large group. The scale of capitalist enterprises can be very, very large. I don't think we've seen the limits of them yet.

The highest level of leadership is technology leadership. It's not simple positive-sum capitalism; it also brings something new to the market. You're literally moving humanity forward. For example, you're not just building an organization that creates chairs (which are valuable), but you are building spacecraft doing something that has never been done before.

As we go from demagogic socialist to nationalist to capitalist to technologist, the degree of difficulty gets harder, but more value is added to society in the medium- to long-run. Every other group benefits from technologists. Planes work. Trains work. We take all this for granted now, but a small group pushed those technologies forward and scaled them.

DON'T ARGUE. BUILD.

> Don't argue on Twitter.
>
> Build the future.

The hard way to gain status is to build something, to accomplish something, to add value. The easy way to gain status is to accuse someone else of being a bad person. It's a status-acquisition hack, a quick way to gain relative status. Your critique of the existing system may be correct. But you need a product, not just a critique.

Don't argue about regulation. Build Uber. Don't argue about monetary policy. Build Bitcoin. Don't argue about anything; just build an alternative. Don't argue with words. Build products based on truths many people can't grasp. If it works, they'll buy it. Their incomprehension is your moat.

People talked about ideas like public choice theory, polycentric law, distributed order, and fiat currencies for many years. Then we built Airbnb, Uber, and Bitcoin, which gave people a short-term economic incentive to understand those ideas. Yes, we can create self-regulating environments. Yes, we can have money without the involvement of state actors.

> Apple disrupted BlackBerry.
>
> Netflix disrupted Blockbuster.
>
> Amazon disrupted Barnes & Noble.
>
> These weren't turnaround projects. They weren't attempts at reform. There was no baby in that bathwater.
>
> When legacy institutions are beyond saving, build something better. And bury them.

The point of doing a startup is to build something you can't buy. Today money can't buy you a trip to Mars. Or a neural implant. Or a medical tricorder. In the not-too-distant past, money could not buy you a web browser, a search engine, or a smartphone. When the iPhone did not exist, people had to invent it.

I've got this idea: "Works in practice, not in theory." So much stuff I saw as a scientist at Stanford worked in theory but not in practice. Many ideas are exactly the opposite. You can study some concepts only once you've actually built products.

Billionaires exist because they can code apps. Bill Gates coded Microsoft's first BASIC interpreter. Larry Page and Sergey Brin built version one of Google. Mark Zuckerberg built version one of Facebook. Jack Dorsey built version one of Twitter. Drew Houston built version one of Dropbox. Garrett Camp built version one of Uber. Bobby Murphy built version one of Snapchat.

Of course, there's some poetic license here. Not all tech billion-aires coded the first versions themselves. But they all had the ability to get a working app out. That is harder than it looks!

SHEER, DOGGED PERSISTENCE IS OFTEN MISTAKEN FOR LUCK. SUCCESS MAY BE A LOW PROBABILITY EVENT, BUT PERSEVERANCE INCREASES YOUR SAMPLE SIZE.

When trying to build something, many people who might otherwise have been caustic critics, supercilious scholars, or imperious bureaucrats suddenly learn how hard it is to build, manage people, and turn a profit—to be the one in the arena.

It is healthy for journalists to try their hand at seed investing, for professors to see what spinning out their IP actually entails, for scholars to try coding their ideal privacy policies, and for economists to actually contribute to GDP.

We are entering a golden age for builders. Consider open source, 3D printing, app stores, and crowdfunding. One person can de-risk, prototype, and accept payments from around the globe.

To influence the direction of tech, pick up a keyboard or put capital at risk. **You can build something.** Those who won't build will just preach. That keyboard is increasingly available to billions of people around the world. They have no illusions about the relative utility of preaching versus building.

> The really cynical person and the really docile person have one thing in common: they never make bold moves.

FOUNDING

Every startup and every project starts as a hallucination. At the
beginning, the idea is a word on a napkin. It doesn't mean anything. You have to believe it can become much bigger than it is.
Always, at every stage, you have to believe it is bigger than it is.

> The founder is usually the only one who has the
> credibility to impose large short-term costs for
> larger long-term gains.

The East Coast of the US is very much about inheritance. It's
obviously about inherited wealth, but also inherited names,
like Kennedy and Bush. People inherit entire institutions, like
the Murdochs, Grahams, and Sulzbergers inherit newspapers.

This is very different from the West Coast model, which is
about founding. SpaceX wasn't inherited. Amazon was not
inherited. Facebook was not inherited. These were built from
scratch.

Founders are selected for legitimacy *and* competence. That's different from being selected for legitimacy alone (through inheritance or an election). Founders start new systems from scratch.

Why is Mark Zuckerberg the CEO of Facebook? Because he founded Facebook. He didn't get three billion people to agree to make a twenty-year-old kid a CEO. Every single piece of support—an employee, a user, a customer buying ads, a backlink—he acquired over time. This was a series of one-to-one transactions where he gave each of them more than they'd gotten before, making mutually beneficial trades. Those resources piled in. It happened fast, as an exponential in this case, but it didn't happen in one incongruous jump in one day.

That's the difference between founding and inheriting—selecting for legitimacy *and* competence versus legitimacy alone.

> The state has far more money than anyone else. But NASA is behind SpaceX because tech isn't capital-limited; it's competence-limited.

Many of our leaders today are selected for legitimacy, but not for competence. Legitimacy could mean they get companies because they are fifth-generation descendants. They could get factories handed down to them. It's legitimate. But that fifth-generation heir could not have built the factory in the first place. If the factory needs to switch from making T-shirts to making masks, the heir might be unable to do it.

Selecting for legitimacy often means the current leader of an institution couldn't have built it from scratch. The seventy-fifth mayor of New York or the fiftieth president of the US is not the same kind of person who can build a system from nothing.

Founders are neither dictators nor bureaucrats because they are legitimate *and* competent. The bureaucrat is selected by election, and the dictator is selected by power, but neither is selected for competence.

The selection mechanism really, really matters because it is not simply the current state of the system but *how that state was achieved* that is important for leaders to understand.

People tend to think an institution will endure just because it has so far. It's hundreds of years old and blah, blah, blah. But I don't think many institutions that predated the internet will easily survive the internet. These inherited institutions are incompetent and increasingly considered less legitimate. There's a loss of faith in banks. There's a loss of faith in the media. There's a loss of faith in politics. There's a loss of faith in secondary education and higher education.

We should think differently about institutions with leaders who founded rather than inherited.

The correct title for Musk, Chesky, Thiel, and other people who created wealth is "founder." The correct title for East Coast scions of inherited wealth is "nepotist." Simply describing people by their net worths ignores whether they *created* wealth. "Billionaires" do not exist as one category.

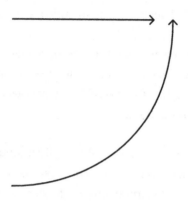

THERE'S A TREMENDOUS DIFFERENCE
BETWEEN BORN-RICH AND BUILT-RICH.

A startup is just one kind of vehicle. It's an important one nowadays, but so are open source projects, crypto protocols, nonprofits, and just individual tinkering. An individual inventor doesn't even need to be incorporated. There are many different vehicles. I wouldn't fixate too much on the vehicle. A startup is an important vehicle in the time and place we're in, but not the only one.

Don't do a startup unless you're ideologically driven to make it succeed. You need something beyond economic motivation, because startups are very hard. There are much lower-risk ways to earn money than a startup. Building a startup is an extremely stressful journey toward infinity.

RESEARCHING

When you decide to start a company, you begin a search in a massive idea space. Are you doing a genomics company? A robotics company? Machine learning? You can use numbers to rank order ideas by current or potential market size, but even that has pitfalls. For something like Uber, if you had looked at only the market size of taxis, you would have never believed they could build such a large company.

At first, your goal setting should be qualitative. You have to have some ideological, motivational, inspirational, or—for lack of a better term—spiritual component as to why you want to build something.

Start out with some end-state of the world you'd like to achieve; for example, youth extension, people on Mars, or building new cities. Your goal doesn't have to be that ambitious. Usually it springs from some passion—often a positive passion, but sometimes a negative passion. For example, you might hate the way healthcare insurance works and try to fix it.

Start with an idea and then look at all the business models that could succeed. Ask yourself, *If this were to work, what could the impact be? Would we make enough money to make this a worthwhile investment?*

You're building the bridge between the qualitative and the quantitative. The qualitative is like the compass heading. The quantitative is measuring your progress along the compass heading. But you can't use metrics to choose *which* direction to go.

At the beginning, goals are qualitative and mission-driven.

Once you're getting ten, twenty, thirty customers (for enterprises) or a few thousand (in consumers), you can start to think about optimizing. The ultimate thing you want is business profit. More specific metrics will lead into your profit based on your industry.

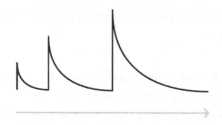

CONTRARIAN IS TEMPORARY. YOU ARE CONTRARIAN
UNTIL YOU CONVINCE EVERYBODY YOU ARE CORRECT.
THEN YOUR IDEAS BECOME CONVENTIONAL WISDOM,
THEN YOU REPEAT.

How do you come up with a good idea?

Good founders don't just have ideas; they have a bird's eye view of the idea maze. Most of the time, people see only the journey and result of one company. They don't see the paths not taken and don't think at all about the companies that fell into various traps and died before reaching customers.

The maze is a good analogy. Sometimes there are pits you can't cross. Sometimes you can get past a particular monster and enter a new market only after you've gained a treasure in another area of the maze. Sometimes the maze changes over time, and new doors open as new technologies arrive. Sometimes there are pits that are uncrossable for you but are crossable for another. Sometimes pitfalls are apparent only when one company reaches scale, and the solution requires re-entering the maze at the very beginning with a new weapon.

A good founder is capable of anticipating which turns lead to treasure and which lead to certain death.

A bad founder runs to the entrance of a maze without any sense for the history of the industry, the players in the maze, the casualties of the past, or the technologies likely to move walls and change assumptions.

A good idea means having a bird's eye view of the idea maze, understanding variations of the idea across branching decisions, and gaming things out to the end of each scenario. Anyone can point out the entrance to the maze, but few can think through all the branches.

If you can write and diagram a complex decision tree with many alternatives, explaining why your particular plan to navigate the maze is superior to the ten past companies who died in the maze and twenty current competitors lost in the maze, you have gone a long way toward proving you have a good idea others did not and do not have.

This is where historical perspective and market research is key. A strong new plan for navigating the idea maze usually requires an obsession with the market and a unique insight others have not had.

> A tech company is about a focused technoeconomic innovation.

Since human nature is constant across space and time, other countries and past cultures are worthy of study. You can see how what worked elsewhere might also work here in our country and culture. Entrepreneurs who know the history of their industries understand which assumptions will be invalidated with new technology.

For a tech company like SpaceX, you start with time-invariant laws of physics. These laws tell you how atoms collide and interact with each other. The study of these laws allows you to do something that has never been done before. The laws of physics encode highly compressed information—the results of innumerable scientific experiments. You are learning from human experience rather than trying to re-derive physical laws from scratch.

History is the closest thing we have to a physics of humanity. It provides many accounts of how human actors collide and interact with each other. The right course of historical study encodes, in compressed form, the results of innumerable social experiments. You can learn from human experience rather than re-deriving societal law from scratch. Learn some history so as not to repeat it.

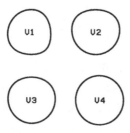

"YOU'RE REINVENTING THE WHEEL!"
MAYBE THAT'S OK. THE WHEEL HAS BEEN REINVENTED
MANY TIMES OVER THE YEARS. A MODERN TIRE IS NOT
THE SAME AS A CHARIOT WHEEL OF ANTIQUITY.
SOMETIMES WE NEED A V2.

Searching out your own path is deeply underemphasized. Don't just look at TechCrunch or Twitter. Some people are successful because they look at competitors and align around the competition. They are just fast followers.

It is very hard to Twitter or TechCrunch your way to real innovation. To innovate, you have to tune out a lot of what the Valley is thinking. I can't imagine Satoshi got the idea for Bitcoin by reading TechCrunch. It was a completely out-of-left-field idea with no previous validation in the tech mainstream.

Tuning out the Valley is often the best way to make a huge impact. Later, the Valley may recognize you're a real innovator. Some of the biggest innovations happen like this. No article inspired Elon to do SpaceX. No one was writing about how space was the next big thing. Commercial space travel was not thought of as a thing entrepreneurs could conceivably do.

Set aside everything tech people are talking about, and look at the rest of human civilization. Look for the areas technology has not moved into yet. That's where the opportunities will be.

If you read about something in the *Wall Street Journal* or the *New York Times* about a technology that is on everybody's lips, it has probably—not always, but probably—started to lose some of its value. A lot of companies are already building in the space, so it's very competitive. The technologies to look for haven't gotten a lot of press yet, the ones still near inception in labs of places like Stanford.

> Whenever a new technology is coming out, figure out how to use it for something transformative while minimizing your technical and legal risk.

The Gartner Hype Cycle is a fundamental concept in technology that I refer to often. You've got some trigger event, and people get really amped about a new technology. Then people try to use it and find out it's hard, and everyone gets demoralized and quits. Then you've got the trough of disillusionment. Those who stick with it through the trough actually make things happen.

This happened with the dot-com bubble. Everyone was hyped about it in 2000, and it crashed. Then eventually, we built all these massive businesses. Carlota Perez describes her whole theory about why this happens in her book *Technological Revolutions and Financial Capital*.

In addition to technologies nobody knows about from the lab, other opportunities are technologies people have already written off. Look for things people think of as "dead" or as not having worked and find out why.

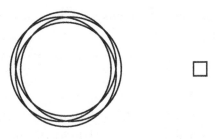

INNOVATION AND CONSENSUS ARE ANTONYMS.
A NEW IDEA, BY DEFINITION, IS UNPOPULAR.

IDEATING

Of all the definitions of a startup, perhaps the best is one from Paul Graham: a startup is about growth. A startup is a business built to grow extremely rapidly. Rapid growth usually requires some sort of new technology that invalidates the assumptions of incumbents, whether incumbent politicians, incumbent businesses, or incumbent ideas.

The gap between stated preference (what is praised) and expressed preference (what is bought) is an inexhaustible source of startup ideas.

> You can condemn hypocrisy. Or you can arbitrage inconsistency.

A framework I use often is the evolution from the physical version to the intermediate form, and then to the internet-native version. If you're into electrical engineering, you can think of this as the evolution from analog to analog/digital, and then to native digital.

We transitioned from paper to a scanner that scans paper into a digital version, and then to a native digital text file that begins life on the computer. We transitioned from face-to-face meetings to Zoom video meetings (a scanner of faces), and then (soon?) to native digital VR meetings. We transitioned from physical cash to credit cards and PayPal (a scan of the pre-existing banking system), and then to the native digital version of money: cryptocurrency.

Once you see this pattern, you can see it everywhere. Look for places where we're still stuck at the scanned version—where we've taken an offline experience and put it online but haven't fundamentally innovated. These are opportunities for innovation.

For things we can do completely on the computer, productivity has measurably accelerated. Emailing something is 100 times faster than mailing it. But a slow human still needs to act on it. One theory: humans are now the limiting factor.

Representing a project online (in something like Google Docs) may not be the huge productivity win we think it is. Humans still need to comprehend all those documents. The problem may be in the analog-to-digital interaction. If we want to actualize as fast as we can compute, zero-delay robotic task completion will be the true productivity unlock. We haven't gone full digital yet. As long as humans are still in the loop, we won't get the full benefits of digital productivity.

Many industries will evolve like this:

1. Human Service
2. Semi-automated service
3. Fully automated

Human, then human/machine pair, then machine.

The pitch of "140 characters" sounded trivial, and the pitch of "reusable rockets" seemed unrealistic, but those ideas resulted in Twitter and SpaceX, respectively.

Trying to reduce a company's core competency to the functions it implements is a thought-provoking exercise. We could see huge companies run by only one to two people providing a single function.

Obviously, Google Search has more than one or two people working on its search function, but it's a billion-dollar function nonetheless. Other functions that qualify: geocoding, face recognition, machine translation. All have a simple input with high backend complexity.

A good question for a software company is: what's your billion-dollar function? For Facebook, it's arguably the function that allows advertisers to put ads in front of users. The defensibility comes from its database. It's likely not a single function today, but it probably was or could be.

This concept is perhaps less useful for companies with significant offline components. Uber's function could be to take in two (x, y) coordinates and move you between them. I guess you could say it's a function where the state it updates is your GPS position, though it's not as elegant.

Each successful platform has to have one "killer application." For mobile phones, it was texting and visual voicemail. Those things pushed people over the threshold to purchase an iPhone, which was a new platform. You can build a billion-dollar company on that user base. Jack Dorsey started Twitter before the iPhone because he knew mobile was going to be big.

That's why he used a 140-character limit for Twitter—it was the limit for one SMS text message. No one was going to buy an iPhone just to use Twitter, but once a person bought an iPhone, trying Twitter had no incremental cost.

From a founding and investing standpoint, you have to consider strategic questions. What kinds of platforms are there? What new platforms cure such a pain point that people get on it? Then what else can be deployed on that platform?

One of those new platforms is going to be crypto. Lots of people getting crypto wallets is good. We can deploy all kinds of new software once most people have wallets.

AR glasses are coming too. It might be Facebook's version three or version four. Apple and Google are also working on them. We might just get a bunch of models at the same time. It's like anticipating the iPhone. AR glasses are an incredibly predictable invention you can start thinking about now.

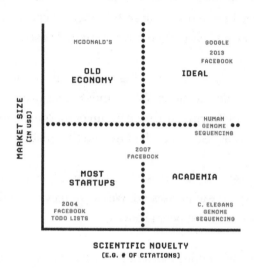

> The best entrepreneurs are logical enough to think of unpopular truths and then social enough to make those truths popular.

If you are using software to go after a physical legacy industry, one option is to do it "full stack."

Replacing just one layer of an outdated legacy stack is hard. Customer acquisition and integration costs can kill you. That's when you go full stack. You can reinvent and reintegrate multiple pieces of an old industry and make better margins. Consider "restaurant powered by technology" versus "tech for restaurants."

With Counsyl, the molecular diagnostic company I co-founded, we found we could not survive by selling bioinformatics alone. So we built a full clinical lab, software, and a national sales force. We had to build a robotic genome factory, insurance coverage, clearances, and clinical integration.

You cannot automate something until you've done it manually many times. Control all of the factors and show technology cuts costs. Remember, for many legacy companies, information technology is only a cost center. They only adopted the code. You were born in it, molded by it. A full-stack entrant into a new vertical is formidably protean. You can morph your product just by hitting keys. Tesla's over-the-air updates for its cars are a fantastic example.

Some specific examples of full-stack startup ideas in a few verticals are law, medicine, architecture, accounting, and restaurants.

→ Full-stack law firm: Template all contracts, use law APIs as core technology, and try to hyperdeflate legal costs.
→ Full-stack clinic: Employ mobile EMR/EHR, quantified self, genomics, telemedicine, and doctors with technology skills. Accept insurance (preferably cash subscriptions).
→ Full-stack architecture: Put APIs at the core of a new construction company. Start with unmanned buildings like data centers to de-risk early versions. Work toward the ultimate goal of hitting the "Enter" key to build a building with drones and prefabrication.

→ Full-stack accounting firm: Given a bank account, auto-prepare it all, from tax to diligence to S-1 with legal sign-off.
→ Full-stack restaurant: Implement mobile orders, payments, and reservations. A/B test dynamic menus with supply chain integrations, and use robots for food preparation and delivery.

If the goal is full stack, always talk to executives in the field early on. A few words can save years of work to identify key cost centers and hard parts. You can start all of these as "just" a new clinic/restaurant/accountant/architect/law firm. Think big, start small. Prove, then scale.

Staging is key for full-stack startups. Start with the ambition to do it all, but pick a specific upgrade sequence carefully! If possible, use industry standard/off-the-shelf for a specific layer until you can get around to improving it.

(corpus?-t)

Anything founded before the internet may not be able to survive the internet.

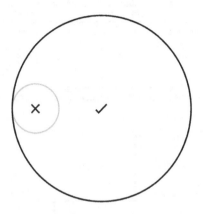

IF YOU ARE CHOOSING BETWEEN TWO PROJECTS OF
EQUAL INTEREST, PICK THE ONE WITH THE LARGER
MARKET. DO THE CALCULATION UP FRONT.

Startups must exhibit economies of scale. If you're doing a startup, you want to go to the moon rather than build a small business. Your first step is to do a simple calculation to determine whether the business is capable of getting there.

Suppose we have a startup that sells units for $1,000 each, and the per-unit cost to produce your product decreases as more units are sold (economy of scale).

NUMBER OF UNITS	COST OF PRODUCTION PER UNIT	REVENUE PER UNIT
0≤N≤100	$1200	$1000
101≤N≤1000	$975	$1000
1001≤N	$700	$1000

A PRODUCT WITH AN ECONOMY OF SCALE: COSTS DECLINE AS VOLUME INCREASES.

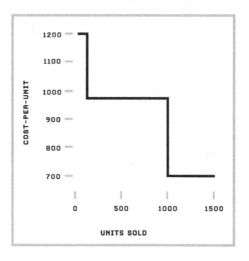

Let's assume an upfront cost of $50,000 for software development to handle the first 100 orders [($1,200 – $700) × 100] and then another $247,500 [($975 – $700) × 900] in fixed costs for design/manufacturing upgrades to support 1,000 customers. After those two fixed expenditures, the startup is paying only per-unit costs like customer service and the cost of materials.

This simple calculation illustrates many things about the startup world. First, we see immediately how important it is to shift per-unit costs into fixed costs (like software) and why what seems like expensive upfront software development can pay off in the long run.

Second, we can see how much capital is needed before the business breaks even.

Third, we realize how important pricing is. If you are not constrained by competition, you want to charge the highest possible price at the beginning to get profitable as soon as possible. A price change from $1,000 up to $1,200 would completely change the economics of this business and make it unnecessary to take on more outside capital. Free or heavily discounted customers generally don't value the product as much and are counterintuitively the most troublesome. Paying customers often are more tolerant of bugs. They feel invested in the product.

Fourth, we understand why achieving $199 or $99 price points without massive scale is so difficult. A real product has dozens or hundreds of cost components, each with its own economy-of-scale function. Each of those costs need to be driven down (via robotics, supply chain optimizations, negotiation, etc.) to decrease the overall price of the product. It's hard to make a profit!

> Everyone's boss is the CEO other than the CEO.
> The CEO's boss is the market.

This is why startups *must pursue large markets*. Even if you can build a product with economies of scale, you need to ensure the market is large enough to reach those economies.

The annual market size is the total number of people who will buy the product per year multiplied by the price point. To get to a billion dollars in annual revenue ($1B), you need either a high price point or a large number of customers. A few different ways to achieve that magic $1B in different industries is to sell the product at:

→ $1 to 1 billion: Coca Cola (cans of soda)
→ $10 to 100 million: Johnson & Johnson (household products)
→ $100 to 10 million: Blizzard (World of Warcraft games)
→ $1,000 to 1 million: Lenovo (laptops)
→ $10,000 to 100,000: Toyota (cars)
→ $100,000 to 10,000: Oracle (enterprise software)
→ $1,000,000 to 1,000: Countrywide (high-end mortgages)

Now, some of these markets are actually much larger than $1B. There are many more than 100,000 customers for $10,000 cars in the world. The number is more like 100,000,000 annual customers for $10,000 cars. So the annual automobile market for new cars is near $1T, not $1B.

Low price points require incredible levels of automation and industrial efficiency to make profits. You can't tolerate many returns or lawsuits for $1 cans of Coke. On the other side, high price points allow for investment in sales. Selling a house does not require 100,000 times more sales effort than selling a can of Coke, but it generates 100,000 times more revenue.

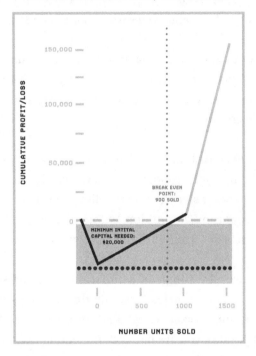

A PRODUCT WITH AN ECONOMY OF SCALE:
GO INTO THE SHADED AREA, THEN PULL UP.

Do market sizing calculations early and often. Market size determines how much money you can raise, which determines how many employees you can support. Assume the average startup employee costs $100,000 "all in," including salary, health insurance, parking spaces, computers, etc.

Suppose you need five employees for three years to come up with the cure for a rare disease. To support five employees per year is $500,000 per year, not including other business expenses. If your market size is only $50M, you have a problem. Finding someone to invest $1.5M to pursue such a small market is going to be very difficult. That $1.5M is more likely to get invested in something with a chance at a $1B+ market.

The best market size estimates are both surprising and convincing. To be surprising is the art of the presentation. To be convincing, you want to estimate your market size in at least two different ways.

First, use Fermi estimates to determine the number of people who will buy your product (top-down market sizing). This requires general stats like 300 million Americans, 8 billion world population, 30 million US businesses, and domain-specific stats like 6 million annual pregnancies.

Second, use SEC filings of comparable companies in the industry to get empirical revenue figures and sum these up (bottom-up market sizing). Bottom-up is generally more reliable. Be sure you are not drawing boundaries too big or optimistic. "If we get only 1% of China..." is a bad start. One of the most convincing things you can do with a bottoms-up estimate is to link or screenshot an invoice with a high price point.

YOU CAN'T SURVEY YOUR WAY TO
AN INNOVATION.

In theory, the ultimate market research is a table with 7 billion rows (one for each human), columns for their attributes (e.g., location, profession), and columns for each possible version of your product, with each entry showing the amount people will pay for those features. Of course, you can't survey 7 billion people, but you can sample a few hundred. This gives you a framework for how to set up your product tiers and roadmap.

Say the first five people want your product so much that they will pay $1,000 for version 1 with features x and y. (Remember, the vast majority of people will pay $0 no matter how many features you add.) You want to earn enough money on version 1 to pay for version 2. If this is not the case, you should rearrange the order of features until it is true, at least on paper.

If you are seriously considering starting a business, consider paying for a demographically targeted survey with 500 responses. It will save you money, time, and energy in the long run. Even spending $1,000 to seriously evaluate four ideas will be well worth it in time/energy savings.

If you genuinely can't afford this, ask ten to twenty potential customers how much they'd pay for different versions of your product or run a poll on social media. You will find early feedback on pricing and features (even biased feedback) superior to none at all.

The 6 Ps are a useful checklist.

Product—What are you selling?

Person—To whom?

Purpose—Why are they buying it?

Pricing—At what price?

Priority—Why now?

Prestige—And why from you?

Seems obvious, but many companies (especially in healthcare) can't easily answer these.

A DEMO IS WORTH A THOUSAND DECKS.

ENGINEERING

A startup is a business built to grow extremely fast. Rapid growth requires using a new technology to invalidate the assumptions of incumbent politicians and businesses.

An internet startup has the ability to grow very, very fast and scale to large markets. It can start in a dorm room and scale to the entire world, accepting payments and providing services to anyone on the planet, without need for natural resources, expensive permits, or human clerks.

> An idea is not a mockup.
>
> A mockup is not a prototype.
>
> A prototype is not a program.
>
> A program is not a product.
>
> A product is not a business.
>
> And a business is not profits.

These seven stages are like a map for making ideas into reality. At each stage, many startups fail to make it to the next stage because of time requirements or some unseen flaw.

STAGE	WHAT'S REQUIRED TO COMPLETE?	MINIMUM TIME
Idea	Napkin drawing of billion-dollar concept	1 minute
Mockup	Wireframe with all the user screens	1 day+
Prototype	Ugly hack that works for single major use case	1 weekend+
Program	Clean code that works for all use cases, with tests	2–4 weeks+
Product	Design, copywriting, pricing, physical components	3–6 months+
Business	Incorporation, regulatory filings, payroll, etc.	6–12 months+
Profits	Selling product for more than it costs to make	1 year+ onward

Startup engineering means getting something to work well enough for people to buy it. Engineering in this sense is distinct from academic science, which requires something to work only well enough to publish a paper. Startup engineering is also distinct from engineering theory of a different kind: planning for an infinite number of users before the very first sale. Between the extremes of zero customers and infinite customers lies startup engineering, where the concern is shipping a sellable product.

One of the primary things a startup engineer does is systems integration—keeping up on new technologies, doing quick evaluations, and snapping pieces together. Some say choice of programming language doesn't matter because a good engineer can do anything with most reasonable technologies. In theory, this might be true; Turing-Complete languages can perform any action. In practice, choosing the right tool or language can be like the difference between going to the library and using Google.

In the early days of a startup, you want to choose the best technologies available and innovate on only one thing: your product. Building version one of your product is unlikely to mean creating a new web framework, for example (unless you are a company that sells the web framework). Outside of your business's core technology, you want to be as boring and vanilla as possible until you begin to make a serious profit from your first product.

> You can quantify the quality of a user interface by the number, type, and duration of user inputs required to achieve a result.

To ship a product, a startup engineer needs versatility. If you are a founder, you will need to handle things you've never thought about before. When you walk into an engineering class, the lights are on, the rent is paid, and you can focus on understanding code that someone made simple for instructional purposes. But when you start a company, you're responsible for calling the electrician to get the lights working, finding the money to pay the rent, *and* pushing the envelope of a new technology no one else understands.

At the beginning you have no product, no money, and the lights are off. Getting people to quit their high-paying jobs to work with you for free can be challenging. You'll need to be able to produce a passable logo, design the first landing page, and do initial sales calls—all while moving technology forward.

When building and selling your early product, sometimes changing direction is the right answer. But sometimes you just need to persist. How do you balance these? One approach is bounded commitment.

List your options, choose your best one, and commit for a predetermined period of time—like a week or a month. Then revisit. This is similar to how sprints work in agile software development and similar to balancing depth-first versus breadth-first in search algorithms. The key is thinking of your time as a resource to quantitatively allocate, like capital.

> SaaS first, code second, hire last.

If at all possible, do your first version with off-the-shelf SaaS tools, even if the interface is ugly. People will tolerate it if it's functional. If you get some traction, you can code a nicer version or automate. Only then, if you can't automate a process, should you hire someone.

LAUNCHING

You really can't be too specific about your first customers. Being specific means creating a spreadsheet with their names, phone numbers, and exactly what you will tell them. Precommit to approaching a set number of customers; then you won't get discouraged if one rejects you. If you get none after you've completed the set, work on a new strategy. (This applies to many things in life.)

Investors care about the future of your product; customers mainly care about the present.

> A new product can never be superior to an incumbent in all respects. Launch means criticism.

To attract attention is to attract negative attention. People expect product launches to be a time for compliments. Actually, launching a product often means people either ignore you or attack you. The attacks come if you are actually solving a problem. Your solution may be ten times better on one axis, but it is always inadequate in some other way.

When you launch something new, people will say, "This product sucks, this company should die, and you are a horrible person." Actual translation? Sell more units.

This is counterintuitive. Why would many of the people who seem to want the company to die actually want you to sell more units? Short answer: because sales give you social proof the product doesn't suck after all *and* gives you revenue to improve it. Over time, skeptics flip.

Longer answer: your staying power shows that haters can't beat you. So they join you (by buying). The crowd's expectations change quickly. Many will strike out at you casually. Later, they will recant, also casually! That's the bit to remember: most hatred is a mile wide and an inch deep. Strip away the negative adjectives and distill legitimate criticism into bugs to fix. Then just plow on.

With most businesses, the main problem is indifference—people don't even care. If you polarize people and 20 percent (or less) who hear about you love you, you can make a business from that.

Every startup starts out cute and wants to become a utility. The rapid growth phase is where startups are most unpopular—and most at risk. Visualize a U-curve on a graph where the x-axis is revenue or company age and the y-axis is popularity. At zero revenue, your startup is a baby, an innovation on a napkin. So cute! No one gets mad about napkin drawings or innovation in the abstract. No one is hired; no one is fired. Praising brand new companies is easy. You start at least not hated. You're on the top-left side of the U-curve.

On the right side of the U-curve are companies that won and won big, like Google and Facebook. Inside an industry you see many companies, but from the outside, people see only the winners. The companies on the right side of the U-curve have gone mainstream. They might be criticized, but they have institutional acceptance. These are the utilities. A link to a utility isn't perceived as an endorsement because the company already won. Using it is no longer "controversial." This is why the government prefers to use big companies. The companies that get links from .mil/.gov sites are the utilities: Adobe (PDF), Twitter/FB (social), and so on.

So, babies are okay to endorse (innovation in abstract), and no one ever got fired for linking to PDFs (utilities are also safe). But in between…

Once your company starts, you will find launch means hatred. No longer an abstract innovation, your product is now taking "their" revenue! It's not just competitors who will hate you. It's all their supporters; the incumbents have marketing teams and loyal fans. They'll come up with good reasons to hate you because a new product can never be superior in all respects. It must be better in one key feature. They'll attack you as deficient on the other features, as unsafe, with no track record. You need to sell anyway—and make updates fast.

Things get worse if your product takes off. Rapid growth means ten times more users than the system was designed for. Everything and everyone is stressed to the max. There will likely be some failures just as the spotlight is on you. Competitors and regulators will seize on them and highlight them.

This is the point where you could get banned for a serious failure. You are all working overtime. Customers are pouring in. Many startups fail here. Friendster, famously. Napster too. PayPal and YouTube both came very close to death—but made it.

The key point: expect peak hatred just as servers are melting. Survive to the utility stage and you win! Prepare yourself for the U-curve.

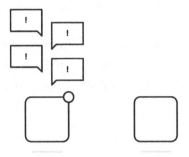

THERE ARE PRODUCTS PEOPLE COMPLAIN ABOUT,
AND THEN THERE ARE PRODUCTS NO ONE USES.

There are at least two models for doing innovation on a really, really ambitious scale. I call them The Paladin and The Dark Knight.

The Paladin model takes something that is extremely popular and tries to make it profitable. Elon Musk is taking popular, supported ideas like solar power and electric cars and trying to actually make them feasible. (One proof point of "popularity": both these ideas were supported by tax credits.) Elon's danger is not getting banned. His danger is going bankrupt.

The flip side is The Dark Knight model. The Dark Knight is like Uber and early PayPal. The market popularity of it, the customer demand for it, is unquestionable. People want to buy from them. But the companies annoy enough people that their ideas are not immediately popular in the same way. The Dark Knights are not going to go bankrupt because demand is so high, but they might get banned.

Those are two different models for innovation on a large scale. The Paladin has to get profitable to avoid bankruptcy, and The Dark Knight has to get to a certain level of popularity to avoid being banned.

> First they'll argue it won't succeed. Then they'll argue it's too successful.

HIRING

In the last generation, Instagram, WhatsApp, Minecraft, and Bitcoin all got to billion-dollar valuations with very small teams. Those were all founded in 2009/2010. We haven't even begun to stretch the limits of capital efficiency.

What I prefer is a tiny team of well-rounded athletes, employees who are smart, hard working, and work well together. Then there are no politics because everybody was selected for alignment.

Finding up-and-coming people is a very important component of hiring. Technology executive and investor Keith Rabois has a good saying: "Hire geniuses no one knows yet." My version is: "Hire people who are hungry and can teach us something."

Hiring "hungry" people usually means finding people at the beginning of their careers. One thing I'm wired for, which isn't common, is I'm almost anti-credential. I understand the value of credentials, but I'm actually most excited when I see a smart person who does not have credentials already, because that's a good value. I can hire them, I can pay them reasonably well, and I can help them level up. I can give them the biggest opportunities they've had in their lives.

I have recruited people in the middle of nowhere living with their parents in Canada, Malaysia, and Poland. I saw that they coded well or wrote well or both. I didn't care about anything else. They were smart people. They could outcode and outwork lots of folks with degrees from Harvard or Stanford.

I'm not saying people at Harvard or Stanford are dumb. I'm not saying anything like that. But from a price-performance stand-point, you want geniuses no one knows yet. When you give somebody the biggest opportunity they've ever had, they're hungry.

Then there's the other bit, "and can teach us something." I look for people who can communicate their knowledge effectively. Can I learn something from their writing? Writing is important in remote work because you engage with people through writing. Did they write their blog posts like mystery novels where you have to read for a while before figuring out what they're saying, or did they put the headlines first?

There's a difference between casual conversation versus writing something for instructions. To be effective, pull key information to the beginning and communicate it in the headline. Then you should communicate it again in the subtitle, communicate it again in a slightly different way in the opening sentence, and expand on it in the opening paragraph.

That's how you should write internal memos. That's how you should write Slacks. State the most important thing first. I look for folks who can do that and who are underpriced relative to their potential.

> We all want to make people wealthier. When we share in risk, we share in reward.

This is the most challenging thing to do as an entrepreneur, but it's also absolutely necessary: hire people who are better than you.

Why is it necessary? If you think someone is doing a job worse than you could do it, you will constantly think, "If only I had time, I could get in there and fix this." If there are high stakes for customers and you have the power to fix it, you feel dragged in that direction. If you hire people who cannot do the job better than you can, you will always feel you should do their jobs instead of focusing on yours.

But, if people are better than you in a skill, why would they want to work for you or work for your company? My answer requires thinking of each skill as a vector.

Let's say you're getting into robotics. You may not know robotics, so you need to find somebody who will do the job better than you could if you were doing it. You may be worse at robotics, but you're better at mathematics or programming or something like that. Then you go to that person as a peer.

You say, "Look, you're a disciplinary expert in robotics. I'm not a ten or a nine like you are, but I have self-studied and I've gotten my way to a six. I can tell you what degrees of freedom are. I can tell you how manipulators work and the basic sensors and actuators. I know some of the problems in your field. I've done my homework."

People who are skilled in areas are actually pretty impressed if someone puts in the work to at least learn the basic vocabulary of their spaces. Let's say you're an engineer working with people who are self-taught. Maybe their code isn't well-structured, but they've managed to scrape some data to get an analysis together and make some graphs and charts. You're always going to think, *Okay, these people are resourceful. I respect that.*

When you and your team have strengths in different areas, there is an ongoing trade of knowledge. This is how I like to recruit. I look for people I can learn from and, hopefully, whom I can teach something. Then we both level up our skills. Then there's a mutual, positive-sum exchange over the course of the relationship.

Speaking of the course of the relationship, LinkedIn founder Reid Hoffman's concept of the initial employer-employee compact as a "tour of duty" is useful because a company is not a family. A family is about unconditional love. That's not how a company is. A good company works on *conditional* love—you have to deliver.

On the other hand, a company shouldn't be completely mercenary. Everybody has bad days. Everybody has a bad week at times, or sometimes even a bad month or more. These are our fellow co-workers, and we have mercy for their challenges, even if the customer doesn't. The customer doesn't care whether someone had a bad day at Coca-Cola's bottling plant. They just think, *Why is this bottle all crushed? I'm going to buy Pepsi.*

The customer isn't acting out of malice. It's just that the interface they're seeing is not human. They see a crushed bottle. There's a failure somewhere in the supply chain. So they just shrug and pick the other thing, right?

The customer is genuinely merciless. You have to somehow buffer that for employees inside the company. I think the intermediate is this concept of the tour of duty: a pre-arranged, clear set of expectations about deliverables, timeline, and departure.

MANAGING

A founder's role changes a lot as a company grows. An analogy from the sports world:

1–10 employees: player

10–100 employees: coach

100–1,000 employees: general manager

1,000+ employees: commissioner

Bureaucracy is quantified by the number of people who can veto your actions. Generally, it should be low. Yet if it hits zero, you have no team. The inverse of bureaucracy is direct personal accountability. Many people quickly find they prefer bureaucracy.

Politics is about the disposition of shared resources. The less that is collectively shared, the less room there is for politics. A startup has few politics because there is nothing to loot within the organization. All resources are outside.

When a small organization is expanding into a frontier, there is little gain from internal politics and large gains from engineering and sales to external parties. This suggests minimizing politics at a company level, which means increasing incentives for seeking resources outside the company. At an individual level, minimize politics by acquiring resources externally by coding or closing a deal versus requesting them internally. One of the reasons an external focus helps to minimize politics is there is much less dispute over ownership. Eat what you kill.

Scale increases the size of the pie, which decreases economic alignment. As team size increases, payoff functions begin diverging and politics arises.

EQUITY UNITES, POLITICS DIVIDES.

Given K people, each with a binary win-or-loss outcome, we get 2^K outcome scenarios. Your job: ensure each person wins more when all others win. Off-diagonal incentives will kill organizations. Politics arises when one person's biggest win involves (or requires!) another person's loss.

> More people, more differing incentive structures (hence problems).

As scale increases, alignment decreases. Eventually, a sufficiently misaligned organization degenerates into infighting. We can turn this into a mathematical model that will predict the optimal size of a network and the point beyond which "network defects" dominate. Network defects are what I call the case when increasing size beyond a certain point decreases the value of the network.

In classic network effects, Metcalfe's law is based on the idea that every node gains value from every other node, hence N^2 utility. Mathematician Andrew Odlyzko argues that it's more like $N \log(N)$, as most nodes don't contribute value to other nodes. But neither model predicts a network size beyond which utility declines.

Leaders should focus on creating, quantifying, and communicating alignment as much as possible. Doing so is complementary to daily management. Alignment is why people do things even without assigned to-dos.

An actual organizational chart is a map of who listens to whom. Twitter has changed the "org chart" of the world. Slack has changed the "org chart" of each company. Who actually listens to whom? That matters more than whatever governance structure is written down on paper.

Both the best and worst CEOs have this in common: the company could run without them.

Before candidates join your company, have them write out what they would consider success, mediocrity, and failure: bull, base, and bear. Where do they want to be in a year or four years?

This is a useful thing for you and massive for them. What would be good, what would be amazing, and what would be a failure in four years? By considering that, they take more responsibility for their own paths. And they'll have fun looking back on their answers four years later. They'll be able to see, "Wow, I was so awful on these predictions, and I was correct on these!"

Use the same technique for dividing up labor between a manager and an employee. Do a two-by-two table with four quadrants: What does the manager expect from themself? What does the manager expect from the employee? What does the employee expect from themself? What does the employee expect from the manager?

This type of table is so simple, but you should create one at every one-on-one, and you should do a one-on-one every week. It completely rectifies miscommunication. By putting into writing what you expect of yourself and another person, you're holding yourself accountable in front of that person, just like that person is holding themself accountable in front of you. Both of you know what you expect from the other.

Tracking the tables in a simple document over time is super useful as a manager because it allows you to point back to what was agreed on, and the employee can do the same. It is not an adversarial thing, but it is useful to keep aligned. Everybody doesn't always nail everything. New things come up. It's not meant to be signed in blood.

> It is not enough just to build. You must also build the power to disrupt.

Product is merit, and distribution is connections.

Coming out of school as an academic or an engineer, you're taught to think about quality of code, quality of user experience, quality of the product. How functional is it? How well does it work for the user? How elegant is it? Product quality in some ways is completely within your control.

Distribution answers: how do you get the product to the consumer? For example, you make a nice tasting beverage—that's a product. But it requires distribution deals to have it in a store, at the front of the store, to have it near the checkout. How do customers become aware of your product? How do you get it on shelves at Walmart? How do you get it high up on the page on Amazon?

Distribution is about connections. Anyone can get commodity distribution (by paying for Google ads or Facebook ads). The art is to find some distribution arbitrage in your time and place. Find an inexpensive customer acquisition channel and pile up users through an underpriced angle others haven't realized yet.

Startup = Growth. If you don't consciously optimize your company for growth, you will be outgrown by a competitor who has.

To maintain a constant monthly growth rate, you need to either keep hiring more salespeople of equal or greater quality (a very difficult task), or you need some way to grow virally through your existing customer base.

Virality gives you the ability to acquire more customers without expanding your sales force. It also means your economy of scale becomes much better because you don't need to spend as much in sales for each incremental customer.

GOOD ENTREPRENEURS BRAG WITH
NUMBERS, NOT ADJECTIVES.

One reason startups are stressful is small sample sizes. You have a small number of employees, investors, and customers. If you're an enterprise company with ten customers and one of them cancels, 10 percent of your revenue is gone. Your revenue was increasing last quarter, and now, suddenly, it is down. Now it's harder to raise money. Now you might not be able to make payroll. Now you are up shit creek. When you have small sample sizes, there's serious stress.

When you have 1,000 customers and one of them leaves, it doesn't matter that much, right? It's bad, but you're not losing sleep. Few realize small sample sizes are where much stress comes from.

When you're beginning to scale your business (when users or revenue growth are consistently growing), here's a piece of advice: include a paired metric of quality to compensate for possible cheating of the main growth metric.

If you incentivize salespeople on the basis of revenue, you also should look at customer feedback, churn rate, and per-customer profit. Ideally, you assess profit rather than revenue.

If you focus on growing users, pay close attention to churn. Pairing a second measure of quality with a metric of growth is very, very important. This is especially true when a lot of new employees are joining the company.

EXECUTING

What does good execution involve, in concrete terms? The execution mindset means doing the next thing on the to-do list at all times. Rewrite the list every day or every week in response to progress.

This is easy to say but extremely hard to do. It means saying no to other people, saying no to distractions, saying no to fun, and exerting all your waking hours on the task at hand.

Executing is about running through the idea maze fast. Think of each task on the list as clearing a turn of the maze. The most important tasks get you closer to the exit, or at least to a treasure chest with some power-ups.

In terms of execution heuristics, perhaps the best is Peter Thiel's "one thing." Everyone in the company is responsible for one thing. Each person should at all times know what their one thing is, and everyone should know everyone else's too.

Marc Andreessen's anti to-do list is also good: write down what you just did, and then cross it off. Even if you get off track, this gives you a sense of what you were working on and your progress.

> Doing things as fast as you can often means doing them one at a time.

How do you rally your team around your goals? First, ensure the goals are aligned with the big vision. You want to show how increasing a quantitative metric achieves the qualitative goals people joined for.

Here's an example from my genomics company. We've tested over a million couples, but testing the first thousand couples was a huge deal. A lot of us had been PhDs working on genome sequencing for years before it was known to the public. We wanted to show the work we did in academia, and all that societal investment in the Human Genome Project was paying off. We'd say we just need to fix these bugs, to work overtime for a few more days, a few more weeks, to reach this thousand-customer milestone. It was our magic number. Until we executed on a thousand real patient samples at a high quality, we didn't feel our scientific work had produced anything.

This is how you align the quantitative metric and show how it is achieving qualitative goals. It didn't hurt we also earned $1,000 for every customer. If we did a thousand tests, we earned a million dollars.

My brother Ramji is very good at execution. He is disciplined and very, very smart. He approaches problems in a different way than me. What I learned from Ramji is a skill or mode called "list, rank, iterate." It's a meta-algorithm, a simple but useful way to attack unstructured problems.

Say you have a problem like, "How do we increase sales?" or "How do we raise capital?" Start by making a list—of prospective doctors to sell to or VCs to fundraise from.

Then do a ranking function on them. "Which zip code is this

doctor in? Is she likely to prescribe this test?" or "Has this VC invested in companies like ours before?"

Then iterate brutally through the ranked list. The key thing is setting a limit. You say, "All right, I'm going to do 150 of these. If I don't get any hits on them, I'm going to try a new strategy." This concept of list, rank, and iterate is a great way of structuring unstructured problems. That's something I owe Ramji.

☑ ☑ ☑ ☑ ☑ ☑
☑ ☑ ☒ ☑ ☑ ☑
☑ ☑ ☑ ☑ ☑ ☑

SOMETIMES BUSINESS IS ABOUT FIGURING OUT
REALLY NON-OBVIOUS THINGS. MORE FREQUENTLY
IT'S ABOUT DOING THE OBVIOUS THING.

When starting a business, conventional wisdom says the idea is everything. People believe that with the right idea, bringing it to market and making a billion dollars is just a matter of details. This is how the general public thinks technological innovation happens.

"It's not the idea; it's the execution" is an excellent reminder, a mantra to keep ourselves in a state of focus. It's especially useful for startup novices or dreamers. Novices tend to assign far too much importance to patents or seemingly brilliant ideas without working prototypes.

Making a product or experience seem easy is really hard. If you're a builder or a founder, you tend to have respect for everything else because you know, "My God, it was a lift to do that from scratch. That was very difficult."

As a general rule, if someone can steal your idea by simply hearing it, you don't have something defensible. Compare "I have an idea for a social network for pet owners" to "I've developed a low-cost way to launch objects into space."

AFTER YOU SOLVE THE BIGGEST
PROBLEM, SOMETHING ELSE BECOMES
THE BIGGEST PROBLEM.

In the early days of a startup, the most important number is the burn rate. Every single person must be indispensable. Eventually, if successful, the company starts building up some structure. Conservatism takes over. With the business growing consistently, the founder adds structure, career tracks, and a stable hierarchy.

The new important measure becomes the "bus number," the number of people who can get hit by a bus with the company still remaining functional. Suddenly, every single person must now be dispensable.

This is like the transition from unicellularity to multicellularity. The founder has to invest in a bureaucracy that impersonalizes the company and turns every employee into an interchangeable part. Otherwise, one person could quit and crash the company.

Around this time, parasites start entering. They don't want the risk of a small startup business. They want lots of perks, high salaries, low workload, and the minimum work for the maximum return. They aren't truly aligned; the company is just a job to pay the rent. The interchangeability actually attracts them!

They know they don't need to pull their weight, and they aren't accountable individually for the business's success or failure. The system will support them. This behavior is rational for them, but it degenerates into entitlement and eventually causes collapse, though that may take a very long time.

Finally, some stifled employee decides to exit the stultifying bureaucracy and become a founder, and the cycle starts anew.

If you don't write history, you will not be the winner.

A startup is willing something into existence. Elon has a saying about startups: "It's like chewing broken glass and staring into the abyss." The reason is there's no place to hide. You cannot blame somebody else. You just have to figure it out. There is no safety net. Your company could die, everything could go to zero, and you could be humiliated in public by the haters.

(Haters actually just hate themselves, though. They are rooting for somebody else's failure because they don't have the courage to try themselves. They can no longer make calculated bets because, to protect their egos, they've convinced themselves everything is going to fail.)

You need some degree of idealism and determination. In building a startup, you cannot be purely economically motivated. At least I couldn't, because many times the rational thing to do is quit. The rational thing to do is quit and get a decent job where they pay you well and you don't have as much responsibility. There's nothing wrong with that. If you're a rational human being, that's probably a pretty good thing to do.

The reason to do a startup is to build something you can't buy. Elon cannot buy a trip to Mars. I wrote *The Network State* because to unblock biomedicine and get life extension technologies, we need to solve the sovereignty problem. I think this is the long-term path to super-soldier serums and other breakthroughs for humanity.

Businessman and investor Ben Horowitz has a great blog post about founders' persistence called "Nobody Cares." (I actually do care about entrepreneurs, and so does Ben.) But I send the post to entrepreneurs sometimes when they need to hear it. Here is the key excerpt:

> "Nobody cares, just coach your team" might be the best CEO advice ever. Because, you see, nobody cares. When things go wrong in your company, nobody cares. The press doesn't care, your inves-

tors don't care, your board doesn't care, your employees don't care, even your mama doesn't care. Nobody cares.

And they are right not to care. A great reason for failing won't preserve one dollar for your investors, won't save one employee's job, or get you one new customer. It especially won't make you feel one bit better when you shut down your company and declare bankruptcy.

All the mental energy you use to elaborate your misery would be far better used trying to find the one seemingly impossible way out of your current mess. It's best to spend zero time on what you could have done and all of your time on what you might do. Because in the end, nobody cares, just run your company.

Mark Zuckerburg also said something like this: "When you feel boxed in, if you're smart enough, there's usually a move." Technology is multi-dimensional enough that there is usually a move available. If you're smart enough and dedicated enough, you can find it.

Business presents difficult situations where you need to achieve the best outcome possible under the circumstances. In fact, you'll often piss off somebody no matter what you do. Now repeat that cycle many times. The job is actually so hard that even as a great founder, you will fail at many things, pretty badly.

> The realism to know what is impossible, the imagination to know what is possible.

EVOLVING

THE PRODUCTIVITY PLAYBOOK

Write out your goals. It's amazing how few people do. By writing out your goals, you prevent a random walk through life. So many people just wander through life.

CLEAR WRITTEN INSTRUCTIONS ARE
THE BEST WAY TO SCALE YOURSELF.

I always have a broad mission or direction, and everything I learn gets mapped onto it. My brain has sort of a single-threaded worldview, which is a funny thing to say because you might think I hop around a lot. But it all has context. If I can't fit something in, I tend to not remember it. I have this mental "clothesline" where I hang ideas among each other. It helps me remember them too, like data compression.

Doing more than one thing is very hard. You can do one big thing, and you can attach lots of subroutines to that. But if you're trying to do more than one big thing, you have to decide every single moment of the day, am I spending time on A or B?

I lie awake at night and think, *Okay, here's what I've learned today. How does that fit into my broad collection of ideas? Where are the contradictions, overlaps, and so on?* Most people do not do this. They just compartmentalize. They'll learn something, but they won't try to propagate it through other things they know to see if it conflicts with other ideas.

Economist and philosopher John Maynard Keynes said, "Practical men, who believe themselves to be quite exempt from any intellectual influences, are usually the slaves of some defunct economist." Meaning, if you don't know what intellectual software you're running, you're running something subconsciously.

> Your email inbox is a to-do list other people write for you. Task length and importance are not related to recently received.

As individual productivity rises, the amount of consensus needed to build something falls. Today a few people (or even just one) can prove a crazy idea works. Increased productivity leads directly to increased individual independence. Higher productivity means smaller groups. Smaller groups means less averaging. Less averaging means higher variation in outcomes.

Higher productivity also means quicker failures. Quicker failure means you can create more trials. More trials means you have more chances to find your comparative advantage. Iterate.

With the internet, your life can begin much earlier than it could twenty years ago. You can fast forward through the demo and tutorial levels to start playing the real game.

IT'S HARD TO SAY NO TO ALMOST EVERYTHING.
NO AS THE DEFAULT. BUT IF YOU DON'T, YOU
CAN'T SAY YES TO THE IMPORTANT THINGS.

> You have 168 hours per week, ~112 awake.
> Substitute capital for time, technology for both.
> Avoid travel. Cancel meetings. Focus on doing.

You can work sustainable seventy-hour weeks *if* you work when you want, sleep when you want, wake up when you want, work out when you want, and never travel.

I want to maximize the total number of hours I can work, including weekdays and weekends. I might want to work for sixteen hours one day, then rest the next day. I do meetings only one day a week. The rest of the week, I am totally free to work spontaneously. That's my single biggest productivity hack: stack all meetings on (for example) Monday and Thursday. Then you are always no more than three days from a meeting, yet you get five focus days per week.

Losing sleep for a night isn't the end of the world. Losing sleep for a year will affect your long-term health. Even from a pure dollars-and-cents perspective, losing too much sleep is going to affect your wealth-generating capacity and your capacity to provide value for your employees and your shareholders. Even if sacrificing sleep seems like the selfless thing to do on a daily basis, on a long-term basis, you want to take care of your health *for the health of those* around you.

Before I started my first company, I was about as jacked as it's possible to be with my South Asian physiology. I lifted, ran, and worked out all the time. Doing that while operating a startup was difficult because there was always the temptation to make that short-term sacrifice, to stay up late or skip the workout to take a sales call.

I would tell myself I have a responsibility to my employees, and I believed my small health goals or hour of sleep wasn't as important as the team's outcome. I had a fiduciary responsibility to them. After all, I had them quit their jobs and move across the country. I didn't want to say, "Oh, we didn't get that deal because I went on a run."

It took me a while to realize this was actually a false dichotomy. Sacrificing your physical fitness or health will also impoverish your team in the medium run. You can tap into that short-term health sacrifice for only so long. In the same way that a short-term optimization in engineering means taking on technical debt, you are taking on physical debt if you are not working out and eating right each day.

I want to put that in the top of my consciousness for my next project. I actually think daily fitness and eating properly is on a straight line to transhumanism and reversing aging. Whether we'll be successful in that, I don't know. But I want to be moving in that direction.

> Don't just focus on economics alone, because you can overoptimize and distort financial metrics at the expense of health.

What you choose to load into your brain first thing in the morning is the most precious, precious space. Perhaps your first few hours should be offline with pen and paper, writing things out. Some offline time is good, so you don't just immediately jack into the internet.

I write a lot of stuff longhand because it forces focus. There are zero interruptions. Later in the day, I take those pieces of paper, a draft of a book chapter or something, and type it in a digital file.

When you get up, set aside some focus time. Now you have at least a few hours each day where you're moving the ball forward in your own self-determined direction. Say you get up at seven or eight, work out until nine, and stay offline until 1:00 p.m. You've done deep work for four hours straight. No one in the world can bother you, no one can get in touch with you, no one can tweet at you. You are offline to the entire world. That's good because you are able to push forward on *your* priorities. Then you connect and synchronize. You push all your updates. Now you're on the attack.

Drive your work forward before the rest of the world rushes in. You know it's going to rush in, but you want to hold it back and drive your focus forward as much as you can, and *then* let the water of the day rush in.

Taking some time off Twitter can be helpful, which I do every once in a while. I took almost four months off Twitter to complete all the final details in my book and get it shipped. Win off Twitter to win on Twitter. Pretty much anything you want, you cannot actually win on Twitter itself. You have to win off Twitter and announce on Twitter.

Hard work is a competitive advantage.

Even the belief that hard work is a competitive advantage is itself now a competitive advantage.

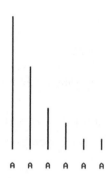

YOU USUALLY CANNOT WIN BY JUST
DOING THE SAME THING YOU'VE ALWAYS
BEEN DOING.

The newest technical papers and the oldest books are the best sources of arbitrage. They contain the least popular facts and the most monetizable truths. What do you know to be true that others cannot or will not bring themselves to admit? There is your competitive advantage.

I read a lot of old books and new technical journals. I'm less focused on the contemporaneous and more focused on finding things that are true but that most people don't know.

Brian Chesky, founder of Airbnb, learned from a bunch of articles written in the late 1800s about rooming houses. Room sharing was much more popular around 1900 than in 1950.

He saw solutions in a sharing economy from a hundred years ago. Then he modernized, transplanted, and used those ideas today. Reading books about societal arrangements at other times and places is a very useful thing.

Technical journals are another source of underappreciated truths. In biomedical papers, you will see that life extension and youth extension for mice is much more advanced than people think. Brain-machine interfaces are also much more advanced than the general public realizes. We have mice telepathically controlling devices. We can do fantastic things with tissue regeneration as well. The technology is here, being held back by the FDA or a lack of distribution.

Technical journals and old books are what I read with intent, as opposed to tech news, which I get in my peripheral vision.

You are what you read.

I was a career academic for the first part of my career. I thought I was going to be a professor. What did I learn as an academic? I learned how to learn quickly.

To learn technical content fast, I just start doing problems. I don't even read the text until I get stuck on a problem. Especially in technical topics, if you know foundations (differential equations, statistics, or Maxwell's equations, for example), you often can start calculating and see where you hit a roadblock. Then you realize what, specifically, you don't know.

Even if you are learning something where there is a known correct answer, it's easier to try and fail than to go and look up the documentation. Reading the documentation front to back is much harder before you start trying. Start, then learn. You have to learn while doing.

You can't really learn something without using it. One day of immersion in a new language beats weeks of book learning. It's the difference between learning French in school, where you're memorizing abstract sounds, and actually trying to order something at a restaurant. You're trying to put a sentence together for a purpose with an unforgiving French waiter who will sneer at you and say, "Lezz just-a speak English, pleeze."

One day of trying to build something with a programming language beats weeks of theory too. If you talk to people who teach computer programming, they'll tell you just "learning to code" is hard. You have to learn to do something *with* code. It could be as simple as taking sales data and creating charts and graphs or renaming a hundred files—anything really simple. Now you have a reason to learn to code.

Learning with intent to use filters down information, and you can snap things into use immediately. That's why I think a purpose-driven life is good. You have a purpose, and you think often about what that purpose is.

Raw mathematical ability is always helpful.

You can understand any mathematical concept in six ways: verbal, visual, algebraic, numerical, computational, and historical.

[handwritten note: do 130 for your finance all count (1.v)]

1. Verbal—explain in words
2. Visual—make a graph
3. Algebraic—write the equation
4. Numerical—do a numerical example
5. Computational—code a solver or algorithm
6. Historical—tell where it came from

A good example is net present value. You can understand it verbally, visually, algebraically, numerically, computationally/algorithmically, and historically. I find that my depth of understanding improves when I do all six. You learn math best with pen and paper, and sometimes with hardcover books.

You can apply this concept to other things. I take an idea or problem and restate the verbal as a sketch, or restate a sketch as numbers. Often, I see things I couldn't before.

Let's say I've got a bunch of complicated deals, like sales contracts with different parties. I'd put them all on a whiteboard and map out what payments we receive and owe at what times. Then I'd start seeing options I wouldn't see when viewing the contracts as a whole.

Another example: the written charter of a company will have various thresholds for who can vote what rights or shares to whom. It's sort of like the House and the Senate voting laws.

A permission matrix is actually the visual distillation of many, many words in a charter. A second matrix would be the cap table of company shareholders. We look at permission matrices and see what is possible.

BUILD BROADLY APPLICABLE SKILLS

At each stage of life, I used my current skill and applied it in a new domain to learn another skill. I never started completely at zero; I was always building from a previous skill.

For example, I naturally inclined toward math and science in school, which led me into academic science. In academic science, I learned the skill of giving slide presentations. This translated well into making pitch decks and fundraising as an entrepreneur. That skill translated into evaluating pitch decks as an investor and a venture capitalist because I knew what went into them.

The academic computer code I wrote for my research was the skill foundation for writing bioinformatics code at my startup. That gave me the ability to architect a commercial system. Each step was like a lily pad hop where I leveraged everything I already knew. I never had to jump all the way to something totally unfamiliar.

Each step leads to the next. You bring immediate value from what you already know and build up skill in what you don't know that well yet. At each step, you have to be ambitious but not unrealistic. Be your own biggest fan and your own biggest critic. Have an incredible degree of realism about your own strengths and weaknesses, and work with others who complement your strengths and weaknesses.

> As an engineer, scientist, investor, or entrepreneur, your theories are constantly tested against physical laws or the market. It's bracing and humbling.

I tend toward discussing theory, but let's talk tactics and next steps because we must also be practical enough to get things done.

The ideal is you are a full-stack engineer *and* full-stack creator. That's using both your right brain and left brain. For engineering, that means you master computer science and statistics. Knowing physics and continuous math is also good. That's actually quite valuable, and you might need to use continuous math with AI nowadays.

Every domain has algorithms and data structures, which means computer science and stats are useful anywhere. You can walk into Walmart and start writing code for shopping carts or basket pricing. You can walk into American Airlines and write code for flight scheduling. You can walk into Pfizer and start on drug preparation and pharmaceutical manufacturing.

A productive mental model just keeps chugging out result after result. If you're good at math, you can do a lot of physics. You can go into fluid mechanics, electrodynamics, or astrophysics and start generating useful results.

Of course each area has domain knowledge, but math, computer science, and statistics are universal languages. I don't mean just learning programming and how to invoke library calls; I mean understanding the fundamental concepts of computer science and really wrestling with them.

That base of computer science and stats is really strong if you understand the theory as well as the practice. You need both, because you need to understand basic stuff like big-O notation and all your probability distributions. Now you can collect data and analyze it, right?

Computer science is theory; software engineering is practice. You could argue probability and statistics are theory, and data science is practice.

Computer science and stats are today what physics was to the early twentieth century. In the heyday of physics, physicists could go kick in the doors of any discipline and be like, "Hi, I'm gonna write down some equations and change your life."

Becoming a full-stack creator is also important. Social media is about to become far, far, far more lucrative and monetizable than people realize. They think it's over or stagnant. But we're just getting started. Many who want to build billion-dollar companies will have to also build million-person media followings.

Establish your broad skill and knowledge foundation, then find an area you want to work in. To choose your specific domain, pick an area you really care about for some reason. Genomics, robotics, crypto, permanent relocation; that's what I did, anyway.

> I'm super bullish on engineering. I think parents should be praised for putting massive emphasis on early engineering education.

Literacy means read access. Computer literacy means write access. Learning to code is more like learning to write than learning to read. Everyone should learn to code because: (1) it's not that hard to learn the basics, (2) it's useful even if just doing Excel macros, and (3) it's valuable in every country. Not everyone is Turing, just like not everyone is Tolstoy. But universal computer literacy is like universal literacy.

For those who aren't good at engineering—well, get good at content. Content is as important as engineering nowadays. Every new company could have a founding influencer on par with the founding engineer. Today, a founding engineer and a founding influencer are building a company. Tomorrow, a founding influencer and a founding engineer may be building a country.

> Build your wealth, then help others build theirs.

Math is often about deep truth, simply illustrated but not easily explained. Confirming that a new business model works (diligence) is often easier than determining why it works (thesis).

Mathematicians and investors enjoy claims that are both provocative and true, established through chains of logical reasoning. Unpopular truth is the core of many investment strategies. It is better to bet on physics than markets, but better to bet on markets than fickle sentiment.

A startup should be exceptional in at least one dimension. It can't be "pretty good" at all different things. At least one dimension needs to be 10 times better and amazing to bet on.

> A founder's diligence is harder to determine than intelligence.

There are different kinds of investors. I have the DNA of a seed investor because, as an academic, I was good at finding great students. As an executive and founder, I was good at finding engineers and other smart, talented people. I'm good at identifying smart, creative founding CEOs.

For other types of investing, you have to pay close attention and spend mental energy to a much greater extent than people think. You're watching numbers every single day, looking for the one moment where you hit the button and sell. I think that's a terrible way to live. The kind of investing I like is finding smart people and helping them level up.

Andreessen Horowitz was a great vantage point to see all of technology. There I learned very quickly about a number of different industries, seeing presentations from some of the smartest people around. With this kind of exposure, you get up to speed very quickly in sectors you may not have thought about before. You learn the problems in each industry. After you see several hundred decks, you actually have a good global understanding of where technology is. If you're operating one company, you need to have a telescopic focus on just one thing.

I've done well financially both from building companies and being an investor. As an investor, you do 1 percent or less of the work, get 10–20 percent of the return, but have 0 percent of the control.

> Due to the constant search for new monopolies, venture capital may be more effective than antitrust at disrupting old monopolies.

Venture capital has many, many faults. But there are a couple interesting things about it. One of the biggest is VCs are very interested in whether they were wrong. If they pass on companies that become successful, they want to understand why they were wrong. They want to admit they were wrong and potentially invest in them now. They have financial incentive for discovering truth, which is uncommon.

The other interesting thing is VCs are incentivized to build people up. As an investor, you want to invest in somebody and make them richer than yourself. Peter Thiel invested $500,000 in a young Mark Zuckerberg building Facebook. Thiel earned a billion dollars on that investment, but obviously Zuckerberg earned many billions. Being incentivized to make other people richer, to build people up, is very unusual.

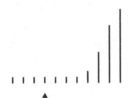

IN HINDSIGHT EVERYONE BELIEVES THEY'D TAKE THE
RISK AND GET IN EARLY. YET, ANOTHER RISKY EARLY
OPPORTUNITY IS IN FRONT OF YOU TODAY.

"Buy low, sell high" is hard because it requires the gumption to do something unpopular. Highs and lows are only obvious in retrospect. In the moment of action, there is only you breaking away from the crowd.

We all like to think we'd have put $25k into Facebook in '04. In hindsight, we all believe we'd take the risk and get in early. Yet, another risky early opportunity is in front of you today. Now digital currency as a category removes excuses for not trying.

integrity

As jobs become more automated, investing may become the most common "job" of the twenty-first century. The 1800s was about farming, and the 1900s was about manufacturing. This transition toward everyone investing may already be quietly underway.

One of the funny things about the tech industry is if you stay in the game long enough and you take enough swings, some swings will connect much harder than you expect. There are investments I made that took five minutes that have returned more capital than five months of work. Of course, investing is still taking capital risk; it's not like you're getting free money for investing.

I've passed on many good financial investments. I'm not interested in something if it's just about earning money. I invest on an ideological basis. I invest in the world I want to see built.

Tech's best feature? The past is past.

There is always another train leaving the station, another rocket ship blasting off.

Found it, fund it, or join it.

We'll have to work to create the future we want.

BONUS

BALAJI'S RECOMMENDED READING

> Kindle: probably a better recreational app than
> Twitter

BOOKS

(Since there are so many links in this section, you may prefer a digital copy. Go to Balajianthology.com to get a digital version of this chapter.)

Math and Science

I do like these technical books. Most people's favorite book seems to be fiction, or sometimes nonfiction. It's extremely rare for somebody to mention a technical book. I've always been surprised by that. Why isn't there a *New York Review of Books* for technical books? Why doesn't that exist?

The Feynman Lectures on Physics by Richard Feynman

Feynman was assertive and intellectual. He definitely was not a passive or submissive nerd, which was the common image of an intellectual when I was growing up.

Feynman showed you could be different. You could break out of that stereotype as an academic. Now I can see that consciously, but it wasn't clear to me when I was younger. Now I can map the trajectory of academic, then entrepreneur, then independence. I can see the trajectory of returns on disobedience, or intellectual assertiveness.

From Feynman, I learned that seemingly simple questions often have very complicated answers. The answer to "Why is the sky blue?" has an irreducibly complicated answer. I also learned the concept of the "cargo cult," how people just repeat things without their own internal checks.

The Princeton Companion to Mathematics by Timothy Gowers

If I were stuck on a desert island, this is the one book I would want because it's basically all of math. It's written by a Fields Medalist who is also an extremely good editor and writer. You can spend endless hours on this book. You can keep going back to it, and you'll always learn something. This is my number one book from a technical standpoint.

Schaum's Outlines by Joel Lerner and James Cashin

This is a great series of books. They're yellow books from the early 2000s that explain different subjects; for example, there's a Schaum's outlines of probability and statistics and a Schaum's outlines of accounting. Many people have studied accounting, but if you give them Schaum's and ask them to do the first ten problems in accounting, it's amazing how many of them struggle.

I use pen and paper, offline, to read and work through Schaum's on a nice table with some coffee. It's very relaxing, almost like meditation. It's like lifting weights; I do it to kind of keep myself sharp.

One Thousand Exercises in Probability by Geoffrey Grimmett and David Stirzaker

This is evergreen. Learning how to do Markov chains and solve the eigenvalues will never, ever not be helpful. This stuff requires more energy to read, but it keeps you sharp.

The Nature of Mathematical Modeling by Neil Gershenfeld

This book is almost twenty-five years old (sheesh!), and there are now more modern methods for some of the topics discussed, but in terms of just packing a punch per page, I really enjoyed this back in the day.

Physics for Scientists and Engineers by Paul Tipler

Visual Complex Analysis by Tristan Needham

I've always liked compendiums.

Visual Complex Functions by Elias Wegert

This fun book proposes plotting all complex functions as colored contour plots. That's kind of an obvious idea, but it's carried through systematically here.

Innumeracy: Mathematical Illiteracy and Its Consequences by John Allen Paulos

The Man Who Knew Infinity: A Life of the Genius Ramanujan by Robert Kanigel

Test-Driven Development with Python: Obey the Testing Goat: Using Django, Selenium, and JavaScript by Harry Percival

It's got a funny name, but it's really, really good. It teaches you how to test things that are bigger than simple functions. If you code Python applications of any scale, this book will make your coding better.

For Founders

Where Is My Flying Car? by Josh Storrs Hall

Just read it.

High Output Management by Andy Grove

Only the Paranoid Survive by Andy Grove

The Great CEO Within by Matt Mochary

The preprint went viral on *Hacker News* a while back. Brian Armstrong and I used parts of this at Coinbase, and Naval Ravikant has used this at several of his companies. We found it helpful!

How Innovation Works: And Why It Flourishes in Freedom by Matt Ridley

This explains how tech founders have always had to fight against the establishment, just like the present day.

The Sovereign Individual by James Dale Davidson and Lord William Rees-Mogg

If you want to find startup ideas, here's the book. It came out in the late '90s. It's the most prescient thing in the world. With most bestsellers, you can distill 300 pages into a one-page summary. This book is the opposite. You can take one page and turn it into a PhD thesis.

It's the kind of non-technical book I actually read and reread with a pen and paper next to me, trying to expand the sentences to extract meaning and implications.

Technological Revolutions and Financial Capital by Carlota Perez

This discusses the fundamental cycle in technology: people get really amped about a technology, then they try to actually do it, they find it's actually hard, most people get demoralized, and they quit. It's those people who stick it out in the trough that make things actually happen. Carlota Perez has a whole theory about how and why that happens.

Indistractable by Nir Eyal

Nir Eyal's bestselling book tackles the problem of modern distraction by empowering us to break the bad habits at the root of the issue. He delves into the deeper psychology causing us to go off track, an ancient problem even Plato lamented. Eyal does this without the usual techno-moral panic, writing, "We can get the best out of technology without letting it get the best of us." Eyal's model synthesizes decades of peer-reviewed studies into a practical tool anyone can use.

The Cold Start Problem by Andrew Chen

This is useful for anyone trying to bootstrap a new community or network, which is virtually every founder these days.

History

> The more history you read, the more you realize that the past is as surprising as the future.

As the chestnut goes, those who don't know history are doomed to repeat it. I'm starting to think a simple annual history exam would gauge a population's immunity (or susceptibility) to a wide variety of deadly mind viruses.

The Gray Lady Winked by Ashley Rindsberg

I give this a 10/10 recommendation. Everybody in crypto should read it. I put this up there with *The Sovereign Individual*.

Merchants of Truth by Jill Abramson

Jill Abramson, former editor of the *New York Times*, explains how business imperatives and pageviews drove the editorial process.

The Journalist and the Murderer by Janet Malcolm

Describing how journalists "befriend and betray" their subjects for clicks, this book is taught in journalism schools as something of a how-to manual.

AI Superpowers by Kai-Fu Lee

Kai-Fu Lee's book holds up very well today. I initially thought it'd be a pop overview of AI, but it's actually a history of the Chinese tech ecosystem. Many of Lee's takes on the speed of execution and innovation have now proven out.

Catching Fire by Richard Wrangham

Fire arguably made us human. This book talks about how the invention of fire allowed humans as species to outsource our metabolism to the fire and allocate more of our scarce calories to the brain. Fire relaxed an evolutionary constraint and made us smarter. We've been co-evolving with technology for a very, very long time, arguably for evolutionary timescales. Technology is actually what makes us human. It's what distinguishes man from animal.

Who We Are and How We Got Here by David Reich

This is the canonical popular summary of Reich's school of thought, along with Cavalli-Sforza's older book, *The History and Geography of Human Genes*. The brief argument is: our true history is written in our genes. Mere texts can be faked, distorted, or lost, but genomics (modern or ancient) can't be.

This book also makes it clear history is a boneyard. There's probably not a single ethnic group on the planet that simply peacefully occupied its plot of land since "time immemorial." One tribe's homeland was once its distant ancestors' frontier.

Reputation and Power: Organizational Image and Pharmaceutical Regulation at the FDA by Daniel Carpenter

Early in my career, I hadn't thought much about regulatory barriers. Most people don't really hear bad things about the FDA. This book taught me why. It talks about the reputation of that agency being key to its power. It's written by an FDA sympathizer, but you can read it through a different lens. The US FDA is the most powerful regulatory agency in the world. How did the FDA become so influential? How exactly did the FDA cultivate a reputation for competence and vigilance?

The Truth Machine by Michael Casey and Paul Vigna

More and more frequently, I point people here for an accessible explanation of how blockchains allow us to establish certain kinds of truths, even in adversarial environments.

The Internet of Money Volume 1 by Andreas Antonopolous

With *Mastering Bitcoin*, Andreas Antonopoulos wrote one of the best technical books on digital currency. With *The Internet of Money*, he's matched that feat by compiling his talks into one of the best books on Bitcoin for a broad audience. Highly recommended!

Seeing Like a State by James C. Scott

If you read *Seeing Like a State*, you'll see there's a sense in which the term "real name" is a misnomer. A better term is a "state name"—a name that makes you legible to the state.

From Third World to First by Lee Kuan Yew

The story of Singapore's incredible transition, told by their leader Lee Kuan Yew. Singapore is an example of a well-run state, one we can all learn from.

History Has Begun by Bruno Maçães

Bruno's thesis is that America is increasingly becoming a virtual society, focused on make-believe above all. I have to agree. This novel vantage point unifies many otherwise opposed schools of thought involving fantasies of the past, delusions about the present, and visions of the future.

The Craft by John Dickie

Anyone working on NFT collections should understand the history of the Freemasons. Many of their rituals could be usefully updated for the digital era. With modern technology, rituals and secret societies could feel like real magic.

Three Felonies a Day: How the Feds Target the Innocent by Harvey Silverglate

This is all about enforcement discretion. In the DOJ, for example, US attorneys have plenary authority in their territories and the ability to press charges or not, as is their wont. You may be familiar with this in the context of the highway patrol: a policeman has the power to pull you over and need not justify his decision to not pull all the other speeding motorists over.

Rules for Radicals by Saul Alinsky

The Prince was written by Machiavelli for the "Haves" on how to hold power. *Rules for Radicals* is written for the "Have-Nots" on how to take it away.

Principles for Dealing with the Changing World Order by Ray Dalio

Dalio describes how today's America resembles the Dutch and British empires of the past in terms of its monetary overextension.

War and Peace and War: The Rise and Fall of Empires by Peter Turchin

This discusses how quantitative methods can identify recurrent cycles.

The Fourth Turning: An American Prophecy by William Strauss and Neil Howe

Written in the mid-1990s, this book shows how a cyclic theory of history forecasts a serious American conflict in the 2020s.

How the Internet Happened: From Netscape to the iPhone by Brian McCullough

McCullough reminds us the tech era is very new and only began in earnest with iPhone adoption.

A Gentle Introduction to Unqualified Reservations by Mencius Moldbug

This is a broad survey of Western historical anomalies, with a focus on the nineteenth and twentieth centuries.

The Gulag Archipelago Volume 1 by Aleksandr I. Solzhenitsyn

Read this book to learn what the Soviet Union was actually like.

The House of Government: A Saga of the Russian Revolution by Yuri Slezkine

Read this book to learn how the Soviet Union actually worked.

Wall Street and the Bolshevik Revolution: The Remarkable True Story of the American Capitalists Who Financed the Russian Communists by Antony Sutton

Sutton tells us how different groups of capitalists funded the communist revolution.

Wall Street and the Rise of Hitler by Antony Sutton

Sutton tells us how different groups of capitalists funded the fascist revolution.

WANT MORE?

If you loved this book, there are many ways to dive more deeply into Balaji's ideas. On BalajiAnthology.com, there are blog posts, extra chapters, audio, and more.

You can listen to interviews that contributed to this book by visiting ejorgenson.com/podcast/balaji-srinivasan.

Balaji continues to create and share great insights:

→ On Twitter: Twitter.com/BalajiS
→ In his book, *The Network State*, available for free online: thenetworkstate.com
→ *The Network State Podcast*
→ In his talk from Startup School, Voice vs. Exit

The most popular of Balaji's podcast interviews at the time of publication:

→ *Lex Fridman Podcast*
→ *The Tim Ferriss Show*
→ *Bankless*

If you love the illustrations in this book, created by Jack Butcher, find more of his illustrations of Balaji's ideas and much more of his work at VisualizeValue.com.

To learn about similar ideas, concepts, technologies, companies, and investments, join the author's email list at EJorgenson. com and subscribe to the podcast *Smart Friends*.

APPRECIATION

This project has provided a feast of gratitude for dozens of people over many years. It's staggering to think how many talented people left their fingerprints on these pages. I'm grateful to every one of you for every moment and murmur.

There are always more names in the back of the book than there are on the front. Thank you to all who generously gave their time, expertise, wisdom, and skill to create this book.

Thank you first to Balaji, for being open to this project. I'm honored by the opportunity to build something around your ideas. It's quite something to trust someone with the raw material of your life's work. I appreciate your trust, generosity, and support.

I am grateful to Jack Butcher for lending his immense talents once again. The illustrations and visuals in this book are entirely his. His work clarifies and elevates every idea he touches. Thank you for taking this project on in addition to all of your own. I appreciate your talent, kindness, and heart.

I am grateful to all of the fantastic interviewers and writers who created the building blocks of this book. There are dozens, but in particular Lex Fridman, David Perell, Shane Parrish, Shaan Puri, Sam Parr, Chris Williamson, Patrick O'Shaughnessy, Erik Torenberg, Tyler Cowen, and Jason Calacanis. I learned something from all of you, and I appreciate you creating and sharing excellent work.

I remain grateful to my parents for every gift, effort, and sacrifice that put me in a position to create this book. You lovingly built the foundation for everything I ever do, and I'll never forget that.

I am grateful for my wife, Jeannine Jorgenson, for being extremely patient with the amount of times I mention Balaji. I am also grateful for your wise counsel, positivity, and encouragement. Thank you for always keeping morale high.

I am grateful for a fantastic editing and design team at Scribe Media, in particular Tashan Mehta (structural editing), Tracy Hundley (line editing), Sophie May (coach), David Arias (cover), and many more.

I am grateful for author friends who share their expertise and without whom I'd have more confusion and less laughter: Max Olson, Taylor Pearson, James Clear, Morgan Housel.

I am grateful to my vast crew of beta readers for their time, opinions, and wise advice. Every one of you made valuable contributions to this book, and it wouldn't be what it is without you. Thanks for the tough love and loving toughness. My deepest appreciation for each of you: Andrew Farah, Tristan Homsi, Daniel Doyon, Jessie Jacobs, Kaylan Perry, Sean O'Connor, Dean Oliver, Andrew Werthiem, Alex W. (& Books),

Adam Waxman, Taylor Pearson, Tim Harsch, Jesse Powers, Johnny Peterson, Sky King, Megan Darnell, Chase Ilten, and Nat Eliason.

I remain grateful to Naval Ravikant for trusting me to create what became *The Almanack of Naval Ravikant*. It was a life-changing project that led directly to this opportunity.

I am grateful to Ivan Edgar Garcia, my assistant, who faithfully supported me in creating this book and, by taking on many responsibilities, giving me time to work. (Shout-out to Athena for making this partnership possible!)

I am grateful to the authors and creators who inspired this book. My drive to create and share this book came directly out of a deep appreciation for the life-changing impact of similar books, a few of which I'd like to name specifically:

→ *Poor Charlie's Almanack* by Peter Kaufman (of Charlie Munger's work)
→ *Zero to One* by Blake Masters (of Peter Thiel's work)
→ *Seeking Wisdom* (and others) by Peter Bevelin (of Buffett and Munger's work)
→ *Berkshire Hathaway Letters to Shareholders* by Max Olson (of Buffett's work)
→ *Principles* by Ray Dalio (and team)

I am grateful for the support of many friends and strangers online who supported and encouraged me throughout this project. My DMs overflow with kind words and eager (sometimes impatient) inquiries. I appreciate every gesture. Your energy helped pull me through the 1,000+ hours it took to create this for you.

ABOUT THE AUTHOR

ERIC JORGENSON writes and podcasts about technology, startups, and investing. His blog at ejorgenson.com has educated and entertained more than one million readers since 2014. Eric invests in early-stage technology companies. (Please get in touch to invest or pitch a company.)

He also is the author of *The Almanack of Naval Ravikant*, which has been read by millions of people and translated into thirty languages to date. He lives in Kansas City with his brilliant and beautiful wife, Jeannine. Join the author's email list at EJorgenson.com and subscribe to the podcast *Smart Friends*.

BALAJI S. SRINIVASAN (@balajis) is an angel investor, tech founder, and author of *WSJ*-bestselling book *The Network State*. Formerly the CTO of Coinbase and General Partner at Andreessen Horowitz, Balaji also was the co-founder of Earn.com (acquired by Coinbase), Counsyl (acquired by Myriad), Teleport (acquired by Topia), and the nonprofit Coin Center. Dr. Srinivasan holds a BS/MS/PhD in electrical engineering and an MS in chemical engineering from Stanford, where he taught machine learning, computational biology, and a software MOOC that attracted more than 250,000 students worldwide.

Balaji has backed a wide variety of startups, including Akasa, Alchemy, Benchling, Cameo, CoinTracker, Culdesac, Dapper Labs, Deel, Digital Ocean, Eight Sleep, EPNS, Farcaster, Gitcoin, Golden, Instadapp, Lambda School (Bloomtech), Levels Health, Locals, Messari, Mirror, OnDeck, OpenSea, Orchid Health, Prospera, Replit, Republic, Roam Research, Skiff, Soylent, Stability AI, Starkware, Stedi, Superhuman, Synthesis, Zora Labs, and many more. Balaji also was an early investor in many important crypto protocols, including Bitcoin, Ethereum, Solana, Avalanche, NEAR, Polygon, Chainlink, ZCash, and more.

SOURCES

Andreessen, Marc and Balaji Srinivasan. "Bitcoin Fireside Chat with Marc Andreessen and Balaji Srinivasan." Moderated by Kashmir Hill. CoinSummit. 26 March 2014. https://www.youtube.com/watch?v=iir5J6Z3Z1Q.

Beshare, James and Balaji Srinivasan. "The Archbishop of Crypto." *Below the Line with James Beshara* (podcast), episode 99, April 2021. https://open.spotify.com/episode/7fpun2Q8XVTkpBzNN3xNko?si=3e953eca7c1c42e2.

Bhat, Tanmay and Bilaji Srinivasan. "The Balaji Podcast." Produced by Jaydeep Dholakia. *Superteam Podcast*, 28 December 2021. https://www.youtube.com/watch?v=q-852BsgNck.

Calacanis, Jason and Balaji Srinivasan. "Balaji Srinivasan (21.co & a16z): Crypto Tokens, ICOs, Longevity, Future Tech." *This Week in Startups* (podcast), episode 769, 10 October 2017. https://www.youtube.com/watch?v=whTJ_q9hxHk.

Casey, Michael, Sheila Warren, and Balaji Srinivasan. "Balaji Srinivasan: Bitcoin and the Search for Truth." *Money Reimagined* (podcast), 23 October 2021. https://www.coindesk.com/podcasts/coindesks-money-reimagined/balaji-srinivasan-bitcoin-and-the-search-for-truth.

Cowen, Tyler and Balaji Srinivasan. "Balaji Srinivasan on the Power and Promise of the Blockchain." *Conversations with Tyler* (podcast), episode 39, 2 April 2018. https://conversationswithtyler.com/episodes/balaji-srinivasan.

Crunchbase. "Counsyl." Accessed 24 August 2023. https://www.crunchbase.com/organization/counsyl.

Dixon, Chris, Balaji Srinivasan, and Benedict Evans. "The Rise of Full Stack Startups." *a16z Podcast*, episode 5, 6 March 2014. https://a16z.com/2014/03/06/a16z-podcast-the-rise-of-full-stack-startups.

Dixon, Chris, Balaji Srinivasan, and Benedict Evans. "Where is the Technology That 'Matters?' Right Here." *a16z Podcast*. 21 March 2014. https://a16z.com/2014/03/21/a16z-podcast-where-is-the-technology-that-matters-right-here.

Elbakyan, Alexandra. Sci-hub. Accessed 25 August 2023. https://sci-hub.se.

Fridman, Lex and Balaji Srinivasan. "Balaji Srinivasan: How to Fix Government, Twitter, Science, and the FDA." *Lex Fridman Podcast*, episode 331, 20 October 2022. https://lexfridman.com/balaji-srinivasan.

Hoffman, David, Ryan Sean Adams, and Balaji Srinivasan. "Rise of the Network State." *Bankless Podcast*, episode 131, 8 August 2022. https://www.youtube.com/watch?v=NEoxETtJ67Q.

Horowitz, Ben. "Nobody Cares." Andreessen Horowitz. 8 October 2011. https://a16z.com/2011/10/08/nobody-cares.

Kan, Justin and Balaji Srinivasan. "Balaji's world Part 1: Crypto, China, Capitalism, and a Decentralized Creator Economy." *The Quest Pod*, 8 June 2021. https://justinkan.com/feed/balaji-srinivasan-balajis-world-part-one-crypto-china-capitalism-and-a-decentralized-creator-economy.

Kan, Justin and Balaji Srinivasan. "Balaji's world Part 2: Network States, Building Cities, The Digital Frontier, and Wokeness." *The Quest Pod*, 15 June 2021. https://justinkan.com/feed/balaji-srinivasan-balajis-world-part-2-network-states-building-cities-the-digital-frontier-and-wokeness.

Lutter, Mark and Balaji Srinivasan. "A City in the Cloud with Balaji Srinivasan." *Charter Cities Podcast*, episode 15, April 2020. https://chartercitiesinstitute.org/podcast/charter-cities-podcast-episode-15-a-city-in-the-cloud-with-balaji-srinivasan.

O'Shaughnessy, Patrick and Balaji Srinivasan. "Balaji Srinivasan—Optimizing Your Inputs." *Invest Like The Best* (podcast), July 2021. https://www.joincolossus.com/episodes/85214124/srinivasan-optimizing-your-inputs.

Parr, Sam, Shaan Puri, and Balaji Srinivasan. "Balaji on How to Fix the Media, Cloud Communities & Crypto." *My First Million*, episode 178, 5 May 2021. https://www.mfmpod.com/178-with-balaji-balaji-on-how-to-fix-the-media-cloud-cities-crypto.

Parris, Shane and Balaji Srinivasan. "Balaji Srinivasan: Exploring COVID-19." *The Knowledge Project* (podcast), episode 78, 14 March 2020. https://fs.blog/knowledge-project-podcast/balaji-srinivasan.

Perell, David and Balaji Srinivasan. "Balaji Srinivasan: Living in the Future." *North Star Podcast*, August 2020. https://perell.com/podcast/balaji-srinivasan-living-in-the-future.

Pompliano, Anthony and Balaji Srinivasan. "Balaji Srinivasan on The Argument for Decentralization—Part I." *The Pomp Podcast*, episode 295, May 2020. https://open.spotify.com/episode/7iuJ6Q7OaNk1TbDmovs5xa.

Ramamurthy, Aarthi, Sriram Krishnan, and Balaji Srinivasan. "Balaji Srinivasan Opens Up about Indians, Network States, Crypto and More!" *The Good Time Show with Aarthi and Sriram*, episode 8, 14 July 2022. https://www.youtube.com/watch?v=oLOr2qBcpns.

Risberg, James and Balaji Srinivasan. "Balaji S. Srinivasan: The Network State." Video produced by Foresight Institute, 21 February 2021. https://foresight.org/salon/balaji-s-srinivasan-the-network-state.

Smith, Kiona N. "The Correction Heard 'Round The World: When The New York Times Apologized to Robert Goddard." *Forbes*. 19 July 2018. https://www.forbes.com/sites/kionasmith/2018/07/19/the-correction-heard-round-the-world-when-the-new-york-times-apologized-to-robert-goddard.

Sotonye and Balaji Srinivasan. "If Einstein Had The Internet: An Interview With Balaji Srinivasan." *NeoNarrative* (substack), 2 August 2021. https://sotonye.substack.com/p/if-einstein-had-the-internet-an-interview.

Srinivasan, Balaji (@Balajis). Twitter. Twitter.com/BalajiS.

Srinivasan, Balaji and Marc Andreessen. "Startups and Pendulum Swings Through Ideas, Time, Fame, and Money." *a16z Podcast*, episode 219, 30 May 2016. https://future.a16z.com/podcasts/startup-technology-innovation.

Srinivasan, Balaji and Vinjay S. Pande. "Stanford: Startup Engineering." Lecture slides for an online course. June 2013. https://github.com/ladamalina/coursera-startup.

Srinivasan, Balaji, Juan Benet, and Vitalik Buterin. "Decentralized Media, a Panel with Balaji Srinivasan, Juan Benet, and Vitalik Buterin." Moderated by Kartik Talwar of ETHGlobal. HackFS 2021, 31 July 2021. https://www.youtube.com/watch?v=vomwbNhmlEA.

Srinivasan, Balaji. "Balaji Srinivasan at Startup School 2013." Lecture. Y Combinator, 26 October 2013. https://www.youtube.com/watch?v=cOubCHLXT6A.

Srinivasan, Balaji. "Book Review: Indistractable." The Network State. 16 June 2021. https://1729.com/indistractable.

Srinivasan, Balaji. "How Balaji Srinivasan of 21.co and a16z Sets Goals and Manages Teams." *Secrets for Scaling* (podcast), 13 June 2017. https://soundcloud.com/geckoboard/secrets-for-scaling-balaji-srinivasan-21-a16z.

Srinivasan, Balaji. "I'll make a meta-observation here—." Response to question by Michael Goldstein (@bitstein). Product Hunt live chat, 27 April 2017. https://www.producthunt.com/live/balaji-s-srinivasan#comment-461482.

Srinivasan, Balaji. "The Purpose of Technology." Balajis.com. 19 July 2020. https://balajis.com/the-purpose-of-technology.

Srinivasan, Balaji. In conversation with the author May 1–May 10, 2023.

Srinivasan, Balaji. *The Network State*. Self published, 2022. https://thenetworkstate.com.

Stebbings, Harry and Balaji Srinivasan. "20VC: Balaji Srinivasan." *The Twenty Minute VC* (podcast), 25 November 2016. https://www.thetwentyminutevc.com/balajisrinivasan.

Torenberg, Erik, Naval Ravikant, and Balaji Srinivasan. "Naval Ravikant and Balaji Srinivasan on Crypto." *Village Global's Venture Stories* (podcast), July 2021. https://open.spotify.com/episode/3oH9nO2TTpQPmpGulKOmQ2?si=c67e56788a9b4173.

Varadarajan, Tunku. "The Blockchain Is the Internet of Money." *Wall Street Journal*, 22 Sept 2017. https://www.wsj.com/articles/the-blockchain-is-the-internet-of-money-1506119424.

Weinstein, Eric and Balaji Srinivasan. "The Heretic & The Virus."
The Portal (podcast), episode 35, May 2020. https://theportal.
group/35-balaji-srinivasan-the-heretic-the-virus.

Williamson, Chris and Balaji Srinivasan. "Balaji Srinivasan—Legacy Media is Lying
to You." *Modern Wisdom* (podcast), episode 519, 29 August 2022. https://open.spotify.
com/episode/51HoWXg2Ju7KuSQg3doLHj.

Made in the USA
Monee, IL
29 October 2023